SCIENCE-BASED DECISION-MAKING: APPLICATIONS IN MEDICINE, ENVIRONMENT AND INTERNATIONAL AFFAIRS

SCIENCE-BASED DECISION-MAKING: APPLICATIONS IN MEDICINE, ENVIRONMENT AND INTERNATIONAL AFFAIRS

NEIL ARYA

Nova Science Publishers, Inc.

New York

For permission to use material from this book please contact us:
Telephone 631-231-7269; Fax 631-231-8175
Web Site: http://www.novapublishers.com

NOTICE TO THE READER

The Publisher has taken reasonable care in the preparation of this book, but makes no expressed or implied warranty of any kind and assumes no responsibility for any errors or omissions. No liability is assumed for incidental or consequential damages in connection with or arising out of information contained in this book. The Publisher shall not be liable for any special, consequential, or exemplary damages resulting, in whole or in part, from the readers' use of, or reliance upon, this material.

Independent verification should be sought for any data, advice or recommendations contained in this book. In addition, no responsibility is assumed by the publisher for any injury and/or damage to persons or property arising from any methods, products, instructions, ideas or otherwise contained in this publication.

This publication is designed to provide accurate and authoritative information with regard to the subject matter covered herein. It is sold with the clear understanding that the Publisher is not engaged in rendering legal or any other professional services. If legal or any other expert assistance is required, the services of a competent person should be sought. FROM A DECLARATION OF PARTICIPANTS JOINTLY ADOPTED BY A COMMITTEE OF THE AMERICAN BAR ASSOCIATION AND A COMMITTEE OF PUBLISHERS.

LIBRARY OF CONGRESS CATALOGING-IN-PUBLICATION DATA

Arya, Neil, 1962-
  Science-based decision-making : applications in medicine, environment, and internationals affairs / Neil Arya.
     p. cm.
  ISBN 978-1-60456-625-3 (softcover)
  1. Science--Decision making. 2. Medicine--Decision making. 3. Medical care--Decision making. 4. Science and international affairs. I. Title.
  Q172.A79 2008
  500--dc22
                              2008013836

Published by Nova Science Publishers, Inc. ✤ New York

CONTENTS

PREFACE

This BOOK explores applications of decision-making primarily in health care but also examples dealing with environmental challenges and international affairs. It gives recent evidence of failures in each of these sectors and attempts to explain how such errors recur. It then describes some medical approaches to decision-making, evidence-based medicine, guidelines, epidemiology, risk assessment, prevention and screening and how they might apply beyond the world of medicine, even to international affairs. Guidelines and decision-making in medical practice are frequently premised on fundamental logical fallacies and questionable assumptions. These include faulty end points, surrogate indicators and a failure to understand the difference between causation and association. Such mistakes also occur in international affairs, and seem to be related to narrowly reductionist, 'scientistic' or 'Realist' approaches, which ignore biases and distortions to objective decision-making. Reasons for acceptance of such failures include perceived self-interest and various cognitive distortions promoted in each sector by corporate use of media, think tanks, key opinion leaders, consumer or citizen groups, all which appeal to fears and uncertainties. Recommendations are made for changes to achieve more robust decision-making in medicine, environment and international affairs.

Chapter 1

THE FAILURE OF MEDICAL
DECISION-MAKING

Over the last fifteen years as a family physician, I have observed developments in the field of medicine. As a graduate of chemical engineering, an adjunct professor of environmental studies and sitting on committees for the environment for my city and for my provincial college of family physicians and now on government advisory panels, I have followed current issues in the nuclear power, petroleum and pesticide industries. As a leader in a physicians' peace group, I have reflected on military affairs, small arms and the arms trade.

Since I began medical school, conventional medical practice has reversed itself on many issues, from beta blockers being contra-indicated in heart failure to being used to treat it, from forbidding breastfeeding because of 'breast milk jaundice', to encouraging more frequent breastfeeding to deal with neonatal jaundice, from enforcing the prone position in newborns to avoid aspiration, to advocating 'back only' sleep position to avoid SIDS, from treating low back pain with forced immobilization, then with active mobilization and finally allowing activity as tolerated.

Such reversals in medical practice are not uncommon and, I believe, represent faults and biases in the decision-making process. While this Chapter primarily addresses such issues in the domain of medicine, drawing on lessons from medical failures to the present day across the spectrum of medical practice, from management of infections to chronic disease cancers, heart disease and risk factors, I will also use analogies from aspects of environmental and international affairs with which I am most familiar.

I will try not to suggest particularly how others should weigh the evidence, but to clarify assumptions behind medical decision-making, to understand cognitive distortions of such decision-making, to consider values that underlie our decisions and to suggest certain considerations to evaluate risk benefit with explicit criteria, in order to make the most honest, transparent and resilient decisions with the best scientific information available. I will suggest how we may design a more effective robust system for making decisions not just in medicine, but in other sectors, including international affairs and environmental policy.

Chapter 2

DECIDING WHAT'S SAFE AND WHAT'S NOT

THREE PHASES OF INTRODUCTION OF A NEW DRUG

The medical "magic bullet", the subject of daily newspaper headlines, is often much less impressive than initially touted. Undesirable side effects may appear even years after its introduction. In medical school, I was taught that new drugs introduced to the market often go through three phases, the three 'P's, panacea, poison and pedestrian.

Panacaea

When it first comes out, a drug may be thought to be God's gift to humankind, curing everything from warts to heart attacks. In fact when we find one drug that seems highly effective for a particular situation, the natural tendency is to look at more general applications. Fluoxetine (Prozac), sildenafil (Viagra) and tamoxifen (Nolvadex), each have been considered, for a time, to be so beneficial that the pharmaceutical industry, certain allied physicians and media declared that indications should be expanded to the worried well, to all men and women with sexual dysfunction, and to all women without breast cancer, respectively, until studies proved them not to possess such advantages. Expensive anti viral drugs such as zanamivir (Relenza) and oseltamivir (Tamiflu), meant for immune-compromised individuals, were marketed for flu-like illness and used for common cold in some countries. Despite equivocal efficacy and dangers, even for treatment of the flu, (including behavioral aberrations) and though they have never been tested against 'bird flu', they are now being considered to be a major part of the armamentarium to prevent a pandemic.

Poison

Later, when major side effects are 'discovered', some former panaceas come to be seen as poisons; if not subject to withdrawal from the market, they may become objects of major lawsuits. Sometimes side effects are discovered early on by the drug company which developed the drug, but as occurred with Vioxx, this evidence may not be fully communicated to the medical profession and to the public for years. But more often it is just that problems aren't discovered until a drug is used widely. The prokinetic agent cisapride (Prepulsid), once considered an ideal drug because it worked on all parts of the gut and was used to treat gastro-esophageal reflux (heartburn) and motility disorders such as gastroparesis, was withdrawn from the market because of its arrhythmogenic properties; it can cause irregularities of the heart rate, increasing the risk of sudden death [1, 2].

Pedestrian

When, with the passage of time, the risks and benefits are properly weighed, drugs often becomes mediocre or pedestrian, something that we recognize when we meet on the street, but don't consider extraordinary, with advantages and disadvantages that must be balanced. Day before yesterday's panacea became yesterday's poison and but today may be used judiciously, in selected cases. In medicine we have seen doxylamine succinate the main component of Bendectin, which was banned, return as a component of Diclectin in Canada, currently the *only* 'safe' agent for nausea and vomiting in pregnancy [3]. The bacteriostatic antibiotic agent chloramphenicol, known to cause aplastic anemia in an irreversible, idiosyncratic way in less than 1:25000 cases, can be useful to treat some serious systemic infections such as typhoid. Even thalidomide, which caused major malformations, now has made a comeback to treat leprosy and cancer [4].

THREE PHASES IN THE ENVIRONMENTAL SECTOR

Similar errors occur in the environmental sector. The organochlorine pesticide, DDT began as a panacea after World War II, before becoming the villain in Rachel Carson's widely acclaimed *Silent Spring* in the early 1960s. Though it is now known to be a carcinogen with terrible consequences for many species and ecosystems, it may be making a comeback in areas where malaria is endemic, where benefits seem to outweigh the risks [5].

Nuclear power, a panacea in the 50s, became a poison by the 80s, following accidents at Chernobyl and Three Mile Island. By this time the issues of nuclear waste management and disposal were unresolved, evidence pointed above ground nuclear testing in the 50s and 60s may have led to millions of premature deaths, and the nuclear establishment was perceived to be secretive with each of these matters. Now in the era of climate change and Peak Oil, it has among its advocates, solid environmentalists such as James Lovelock, developer of the Gaia hypothesis [6][1].

PUBLIC HEALTH AND ENVIRONMENTAL MEASURES THAT REMAIN LIFE-SAVERS AND THOSE THAT REMAIN KILLERS

But not all interventions have balanced effects. Even though sometimes procedures may be carried to an extreme, there are many public health measures whose benefits become more apparent as the years go on. Despite the skepticism of much of 19th century society [7] and Semmelweiss' colleagues at the Vienna Allgemeines Krankenhaus who rejected his advice for years, hand-washing and hygiene on the obstetrics ward led to major reductions in mortality [8]. Speed limits, seatbelts, crash helmets, air bags, and penalties for drinking and driving all have helped decrease morbidity and mortality, far more than medical practice.

Clearly there are some drugs and therapies that remain 'poisons', never becoming 'pedestrian' because of major adverse or unacceptable effects, Lasser [9] found that of 548 new chemical entities approved by the FDA between 1975 and 1999, 45 (8.2%) acquired a black box warning and 16 (2.9%) were pulled

---

[1] The hypotheses central to the thinking of environmental ethics views the earth as a self-regulating living system that maintains the conditions for the perpetuation of life. The earth has finite resources, sustainability limits. Human beings have a responsibility as stewards, to preserve the function of this within the various delicate margins necessary for life.

from the market. The estimated probability over a 25 year period, of acquiring a new black box warning or being withdrawn from the market was 20%.

In the environmental sector, types of poisons are also multifold. Persistent organic pollutants (POPs) which bioaccumulate are banned under the 2001 Stockholm protocol;[2] [10, 11] so are chlorofluorocarbons (CFCs) under the 1987 Montreal protocol [12]. Reduction of exposure to asbestos, has led to decrease in mesothelioma. Mercury in water and lead in paints and gas have few redeeming qualities. Cosmetic use of pesticides (to kill weeds in lawns and gardens to create 'healthy' lawns) has few benefits and carries uncertain risks and is becoming unacceptable in many western countries [13].

The three phases of societal perception of drugs, chemical substances in household and industrial usage and new technologies may reflect evolution in scientific knowledge.

However is there a basis for rational decision-making, a way to determine what may be a true panacea, what is a real poison and what is somewhere in between much earlier on, or must we remain guinea pigs losing lives as science progresses?

---

[2] This class of long-lasting and dangerous chemicals is based on the criteria of toxicity, persistence, bioaccumulation, and long-range transport and includes polychlorinated biphenyls (PCBs), dioxins, furans and nine pesticides

Chapter 3

SCIENCE AND SCIENTISM

SCIENCE

The scientific ideal is a relatively simple iterative process of observation, hypothesis development and hypothesis testing producing new evidence and debate leading to conclusions that are increasingly refined and reliable and cover more situations though are never certain.

By contrast, the sociological process of the diffusion of new beliefs is more complex. This sociological process often involves power struggles in which all sides of the debate claim that their old opinion is supported by the best evidence, but overlooking flaws in evidence that supports their opinions whilst discounting evidence that does not. Demosthenes once said that *"Nothing is easier than self-deceit. For what each man wishes, that he also believes to be true"* [14]. It is normal to wish to be proven to have been right all along and that wish can blind us to the reality that we were wrong from the start.

Some people regard the panacea, poison, pedestrian sequence as evidence of something wrong with the scientific ideal. People may believe that their belief that a new drug is a panacea is justified by science, but science never justifies such beliefs. However when a drug is new there is very limited evidence available- the only valid scientific conclusion is that it is not yet known if the drug is a panacea, a poison, or pedestrian. While we cannot blame science for its misuse, for extrapolations beyond the evidence, for claims that it supported the false beliefs, we must realize that when key constituencies have something to gain, hyping of the value of therapies is common.

The beliefs given as examples above, (beta blockers in heart failure, breast feeding, prone position), were due to overconfident misinterpretation of inadequate evidence. Sometimes science had it right on the benefits, but was missing or underestimating toxicity based on inadequate information (cisapride) or we knew about the benefits and downsides, but didn't have an appropriate view of the balance (chloramphenicol).

SCIENTISM

I too, am a believer in science and the scientific method, but not in 'Scientism', which I will define as the generalized, unexamined belief in narrowly, 'evidence—based', reductionist, scientific studies on which the above faulty decisions were made [15]. Scientism is more religion than science and distorts our ability to weigh evidence and act in our longer-term interests. It involves the unintentional, over-enthusiastic use of data without looking at its assumptions, sources, their vested interests, biases and even deliberate, fraudulent manipulation of the data.

Scientism's True Believers remain convinced that, despite major failures in decision-making based on such 'science' in the past, in the future, medical science, scientific experts or the military will solve each of the world's problems; from medical diseases as cancer and heart disease to environmental and social problems such as pollution, climate change, hunger or poverty to the political and security problems of ridding the world of dangers of weapons of mass destruction and terrorism.

I will argue that many errors we in medicine have made were not merely part of scientific development and either predictable or knowable much earlier. I have seen similar assurances that decision-making is better in the environmental and military sectors despite various environmental failures and now with major US military debacles in Iraq and arguably, in Afghanistan. In each sector, with each failure or reversal, the name and tools change slightly, but the basic methods do not change. When analogous failures continue to occur over and over in several sectors, it may suggest a collective failure of societal memory, and of decision-making.

Even in the couple of months it was found that the majority of angioplasties, (one million in the US annually at costs of billions of dollars, added little to optimal medical management of stable patients, that a recent class of diabetic medications, the thiazolidinediones, may be dangerous increasing heart attacks and eye problems, which good control of diabetes was meant to help.-These will be discussed in more detail later.

In the 19th century studies of 'time proven' treatments of bleeding, cupping, purging and enemas compared to bed rest, nutrition, and observation for conditions such as typhoid fever and delirium tremens found doing nothing to be superior leading to an era of "therapeutic nihilism" [16]. But I am not advocating inaction.

Through a decade and a half of decision-making in general practice, a healthy skepticism has served me well. Before prescribing drugs, both new and old, I had explained risks and possible drawbacks, both known and unknown. Despite many drug recalls and re-labeling of even common drugs, I have never had to re-call patients to tell them that I had inadvertently given them a dangerous drug. I will try to draw on such experience to help assess for example, in what situations a drug is likely to do more good than harm.

Such an approach might equally be applied to other sectors of decision-making as opposed to a current 'scientistic' approach where each reversal seems novel and unpredictable. In designing a better system, it is helpful to look at how decisions are currently made.

Chapter 4

Objectivity in Medical Decision-Making

Decision-Making

Decision-making is a cognitive process of making a selective judgment or choice. It. typically follows a process where a problem or opportunity is identified, aims are determined, relevant information gathered, alternatives developed and evaluated. On this basis, a decision is made to implement the best alternative. Subsequently there is follow-up and evaluation. Depending on the situation, this may be a more cyclical process. Structured, rational decision making is a must for all science-based professions, where specialists apply their knowledge in a given area to making informed decisions. The reasoning process may be based on explicit or tacit assumptions, ideas or opinions and usually defines a course of action.

Medical decision-making often involves making a particular diagnosis and/or selecting an appropriate treatment. So how are objective decisions made in medicine?

Evidence-Based Medicine

The term Evidence-Based Medicine (EBM) was coined by the McMaster University research group led by David Sackett and Gordon Guyatt. and first entered the medical literature in Guyatt's 1991 paper entitled 'Evidence-Based Medicine' [17]. Guyatt's aim was to differentiate clinical decision-making based on evaluation of evidence from obedience to dogma. The *British Medical Journal* now considers Evidence-Based Medicine to be among the top 15 medical innovations since 1840 [18].

EBM is a conscientious, explicit, judicious and systematic process of finding, appraising, and using current best evidence from scientific studies and integrating that with clinical experience and information about an individual patient's condition, values and preferences.

The fundamental precepts of EBM include beginning with an open mind and formulating a clear and appropriate clinical question regarding a patient's problem, finding and critically appraising relevant data for its validity and usefulness and applying judgements about the inductive quality of evidence.

> "By best available external clinical evidence we mean clinically relevant research, often from the basic sciences of medicine, but especially from patient-centered clinical research into the accuracy and precision of diagnostic tests (including the clinical examination), the power of prognostic markers, and the efficacy and safety of therapeutic, rehabilitative, and preventive regimens." [19]

DEVELOPING GUIDELINES IN MEDICINE

Out of the best available evidence, experts ideally may develop clinical practice guidelines (CPGs), which may be integrated with clinical expertise and patient values in order to make decisions. One set of guidelines, *The Medical Letter on Drugs and Therapeutics* has provided relatively independent, unbiased, critical evaluations of new drugs and sometimes, older drugs when important new information becomes available since 1959. Occasionally new non-drug treatments or diagnostic aids are reviewed. *The Medical Letter* receives no pharmaceutical revenue nor allows any drug advertising in the publication.

The Cochrane Centres of evidence-based medical research, and the international organization, the Cochrane Collaboration, named after Scottish epidemiologist Archie Cochrane, author of *Effectiveness and Efficiency: Random Reflections on Health Services* (1972), focuses on studies with the best methods for answering the question including best qualitative studies, and meta-analyses. The Cochrane Database of Systematic Reviews synthesizes such evidence, providing overall assessment based on the best relevant well conducted individual studies, so researchers can then critically analyze and assess the quality and relevance of the evidence [20]. Cochrane reviewers have explicit instructions not to make recommendations but to summarize information, searching the literature according to a pre-specified system to minimize bias. Unfortunately the Cochrane Reviews are still far from comprehensive and many important questions in Medicine have yet to be subjected to Cochrane scrutiny.

There are benefits to ensuring a consistent acceptable standard of care. Medical students and physicians often want guidelines and algorithms including immunization schedules, lipid and hypertension management guidelines, which they feel improves their decision-making efficiency and patient care [21]. They understand that these may change when new evidence becomes available.

Medical algorithms may include computations, formulae, nomograms, or tables, useful in healthcare, but usually employs flow charts (i.e., if symptoms A, B, and C are evident, then use treatment X) or binary decision trees (if X do Y, if not X, do Z). Decision trees analysis may begin with all the options then splits into all the possible outcomes giving each a probability and a utility.

Most Western countries have national bodies for developing medical management guidelines. These bodies, for example, exist in Canada [22], the US [23], Britain [24], France [25], and Germany [26] to name just a few. International bodies such as the Guidelines International Network compile national guidelines. Such compilations also demonstrate that even evaluating the same evidence may lead to different conclusions resulting in varied guidelines among countries [27].

The Canadian Task Force on the Periodic Health Examination [28], begun in 1976, and used a standardized methodology for evaluating the effectiveness of preventive health care interventions and for developing clinical practice guidelines based on the evidence from published medical research. The rules were refined in collaboration with the U.S. Preventive Services Task Force (USPSTF) [29] in the 1980s and the latter's efforts continue. The basic premise- to form recommendations of graded strength based on the quality of published medical evidence remains unaltered. Grades of Recommendations vary from 'Good evidence' to support the recommendation that the condition be specifically considered in a General Physical Examination (PHE), to 'fair evidence' to 'Good evidence' to support the recommendation that the condition be specifically excluded from consideration from a PHE. The latest development in rating quality of evidence and strength of recommendations (the GRADE approach) was introduced in 2004 [30] and so far has been endorsed by WHO, Cochrane, UpToDate, NICE, ACP, BMJ, and 10 other major guideline groups.

EPIDEMIOLOGY IN MEDICINE

Epidemiology and biostatistics are fundamental to the science of medical decision-making. Last defines epidemiology as *"the study of the distribution and determinants of health-related states or events in a specified population and the application of this study to the control of health problems."*

Hippocrates said *"To know the cause of a disease and to understand the use of the various methods by which disease may be prevented amounts to the same thing in effect as being able to cure the malady."* [31]

An epidemiologist determines frequencies and patterns of disease, causes of disease, mode of transmission and factors related to susceptibility, exposure and risk. Clinical medicine focuses on treating sick patients while public health, the sector of medicine based on epidemiology, focuses on reducing disease in the future. Common goals of each may be to prevent disease, improve disease outcome, and to promote the health of populations, but perspectives differ in clinical and public health sciences. Data collection for the clinician is primarily the history, physical exam and technological investigations, but for the epidemiologist, surveillance and analyses. A clinician treats individuals one at a time, which may ultimately impact the community but an epidemiologist examines benefits of community interventions, which may ultimately impact individuals.

In medicine, epidemiology may help to describe the natural history of disease, identify individual risks, and search for causes. Epidemiology identified associations of sudden infant death syndrome with sleeping on the side or prone, mesothelioma with asbestos, use of the oral contraceptive pill (OCP) with increased risk of DVT, and fluoridated water supplies with lack of cavities. In public health it may be used to study historical patterns, assess the health of the community, or evaluate health services.

In 1965 Bradford Hill [32] examined criteria to determine whether there was a probable causation between for example, smoking and lung cancer. He asserted that the greater the *Strength of Association* the more likely it is causal; *Consistency* across a variety of populations, times and circumstances with multiple studies and study designs will enhance this conclusion; *Specificity* of a single type of exposure with a single disease will strengthen the chance of causation (but the absence doesn't refute it); *Temporality*-the exposure must take place before disease (cross sectional and case control studies can't establish causality); there may be a *Biological gradient* (increasing the dose resulting in an increasing response), but there may also be a minimum dose threshold before which no effect is noted; *Plausibility* is based on existing biological and social models, but having a plausible 'explanation' for the relationship is not essential, since putative explanations for observed phenomena often turn out to be wrong; there must be *Coherence*-it must not contradict what it known, though we must be prepared to reinterpret what is known; analogy with other diseases similarly strengthens associations.

The links between exposures and outcomes are complex in medicine, but even more so with environmental issues and international affairs. The simplest situation to analyze is single agent cause and single effect that has no other causes. A slightly more complex framework is the epidemiological triad involving host, agent and environment. However for many environmental or social problems, causal pies full of necessary and sufficient causes or webs of causation are more accurate.

Epidemiologic studies typically look for a common association between exposures and outcomes for a defined population. Study designs may differ in terms of data collection methods, timing, units of observation and subjects. Cases studies and case series and cross sectional studies seek association; ecologic and case control studies are somewhat stronger and generate hypotheses. Cohort studies may be prospective or retrospective and generate more information on the incidence and natural history of disease. Cohort studies are also critical in defining associations between environmental occupational or drug exposures and specific diseases.

Non-randomized trials, opinions of respected authorities based on clinical experience, descriptive studies, or reports of expert committees each have their place but for treatment–oriented questions, the 'gold standard' test, from an experimental or statistical point of view, with highest levels of evidence to test an intervention's ability to affect the natural history of a disease, is a properly designed randomized controlled trial [33].[3] RCTs are often quite expensive to conduct and either prove impractical or require smaller sample sizes. Meta-analyses are meant to draw experience of several similar studies to increase the power of studies and systematic reviews.

---

[3]   Sackett et al. further state, "Evidence based medicine is not restricted to randomized trials and meta-analyses. It involves tracking down the best external evidence with which to answer our clinical questions." "Because the randomized trial, and especially the systematic review of several randomized trials, is so much more likely to inform us and so much less likely to mislead us, it has become the"gold standard" for judging whether a treatment does more good than harm. However, some questions about therapy do not require randomized trials (successful interventions for otherwise fatal conditions) or cannot wait for the trials to be conducted."

RISK ASSESSMENT

Often in medicine, environmental and international affairs, we are left with trying to determine risk and benefits of choices-for example whether to use a drug or chemical. Policy makers also have to make decisions on whether to allow or force withdrawal of a drug on market, whether or not to ban a pesticide or to promote alternative energy sources, whether to choose military action or diplomatic means to achieve goals.

Risk assessment is the process of quantifying the probability of a harmful effect from certain human activities to individuals or populations and the classification of hazards including estimate of risks and uncertainties. *Risk evaluation* is concerned with assessing probability and impact of individual risks, taking into account any interdependencies or other factors outside the immediate scope under investigation: *Risk management* concerns evaluation and implementation of options based on scientific, political and socio-cultural considerations.

On safety issues in Public Health or in industry, risk assessment begins with identification of the hazard (circumstances which result in adverse outcome), quatification of exposure and assessment of response. Probability is the evaluated likelihood or frequency of a particular outcome actually happening. Impact is the evaluated effect or result of a particular outcome actually happening. Risk is a product of the probability and the impact.

Responses to risk include prevention-terminating the risk, reduction-treating the risk to limit its impact to acceptable levels, transferring the risk- passing it to third party via, for instance, an insurance policy and accepting or tolerating the risk. The last choice may be made because nothing can be done at a reasonable cost to mitigate it or the likelihood and impact of the risk occurring are at an acceptable level. In that case contingency plans may be developed with actions planned and organized to come into force, if and when the risk occurs. We need to understand that in some circumstances, particularly in the social realm, risk is more difficult to evaluate, but nonetheless controllable and we might attempt to reduce harm. More complex models would include benefits and consider the nature and probability of each benefit and harm, attempting to maximize benefits and minimize harms.

"PREVENTION" AND SCREENING IN MEDICINE

Confusingly, the term prevention which implies reducing risk to zero is generally used to mean merely reducing risks. In medicine it is preferable and often cheaper, to reduce risks where possible, rather than reacting to full- blown disease. Important preventable health deficits such as lung cancer, cirrhosis and melanoma, which may be mitigated simply by reduced exposure to the causative smoking, alcohol and sun respectively. Increasing exercise, decreasing meat consumption and increasing fiber in diet are generally useful preventive measures to improve health. However sometimes the "prevention" is worse than the disease. This can occur when the "preventative" activity is expensive and/or poorly effective and/or has its own risks.

"Primary prevention" refers to the prevention of diseases, reducing exposure to risk factors before their biological onset: Examples include pasteurization and immunization. Sometimes *"primordial prevention,"* is used to refer to modification or elimination of risk factors or behaviors prior to them causing a problem. *"Secondary prevention"* refers to the prevention of clinical illness through the early detection prior to symptoms that, if left undetected, would likely become clinically apparent and harmful. This is often referred to as *"screening."* *"Tertiary prevention"* refers to the prevention of disease progression and additional disease complications after overt clinical diseases are manifest [34]. Confusingly many doctors use the term secondary prevention for tertiary prevention.

'Screening' refers to a technique for the presumptive identification of people with early disease by application of tests to separate those within a broad population who are likely to suffer from a particular condition from those without a condition. These tests, which include procedures such as mammograms and PAP smears, are meant to diagnose disease at a pre-symptomatic or early symptomatic stage when intervention may alter the natural course of the disease.

A suitable disease is an important health problem which, if left untreated, goes on to serious consequences, one where early detection in asymptomatic persons leads to a significantly better outcome related to response to treatment or to individuals changing their lifestyle in a protective way.

A suitable test is one with few side effects and the ability to detect accurately with low false negative and false positive rates and is cost effective. A reliable screening test gives the same test result each time a test is done while a valid test gives the correct result each time. A sensitive test correctly detects cases, while a specific one correctly identifies non-cases. A test with inadequate sensitivity means a significant proportion of persons with the disorder will escape detection. Such false negative results may give a false sense of security, resulting in inadequate attention to risk reduction and delays in seeking medical care even after warning symptoms become present. An excessively sensitive test will mean that many normal people (false positives) are caught in the net and subjected to unnecessary and potentially dangerous additional testing and/or treatment.

Chapter 5

SCIENCE-BASED DECISION-MAKING IN INTERNATIONAL AFFAIRS

The powerful methods of EBM applied judiciously to other sectors

EVIDENCE-BASED INTERNATIONAL AFFAIRS

In specific instances such as Bosnia or Sierra Leone in the early 90s or East Timor over the last quarter of the 20th century, early military intervention by the international community may arguably have done more good than harm for the survival and well being of the majority of people in the area. Yet, generalizing successes of possible military ventures to other situations or using the military for tasks for which it was not designed, from delivering aid, to conflict resolution, to policing to post-conflict rebuilding and development of schools, water supply, electricity and sewage may not be the most efficient use of resources.

In an article appearing just prior to the 2003 Iraq war entitled 'Ask the Right Questions', I attempted to apply precepts of evidence-based medicine and risk assessment to evaluating the merits of the war to see if using EBM techniques might lead US and British leaders to draw different conclusions about Saddam Hussein and Iraq [35]. The questions 'they' appeared to be asking were 'Is Saddam Hussein a liar and does he hang out with a bad crowd? and Does Saddam Hussein defy international order and like weapons of mass destruction?'

I proposed instead, that before launching a war the Bush administration and the American public ought to ask clear and appropriate questions according to EBM — 'How imminent and credible is the threat? What will this do to the Iraqi people? What will this do for countries and peoples in the region? What will it do for our own safety? What will this do to the economy? What will it do to international institutions? What are alternatives?'

After analyzing answers to the above using the best available evidence, it appeared that the chance of usable WMD that could be any threat to those in the region or as claimed by some to US and IK territory in the near future were nil. The conclusions were most likely that the war could only be bad for the Iraqi people with damage predicted by others, that it was likely to be destabilizing for the region and to promote terror (rather than acting in a domino way to promote democracy) and to cost over $50-200 billion (a major underestimate), and undermine any sense of international governance. Other goals to ensuring adequate energy supplies could have been accomplished more cheaply by conservation.

I then proposed alternatives to war[4] concluding, "These are cheaper, more effective and sustainable alternatives to war. Let's choose them; let's choose peace."

Of course, the decision-making of the Bush administration involved not only explicit logic, but included values, ideology and politics and perhaps self-deception. In spite of the objective evidence for lack of benefits for Americans or the international community let alone Iraqis, whether it was oil, the mutual hatred of Saddam and the senior Bushes, the symbol of Saddam remaining in power for the region, the chance to democratize the Middle East through a domino effect, the Bush administration drew different conclusions. Similar analyses could have been done in Afghanistan [36].

---

[4]   These included 1. supporting international law, multilateral processes and institutions: the International Criminal Court, the Biological Weapons Convention, the Anti-Ballistic Missile treaty, Landmines Treaty, and even the Kyoto Protocol to reduce our dependence on fossil fuels 2. de-linking military sanctions from economic sanctions 3. supporting regional arms control 4.genuine moves on the part of the Nuclear Weapons States to abolish nuclear weapons as mandated by Article VI of the Nuclear Non-Proliferation Treaty to reduce the threat of proliferation and support for inspection and verification regimes to get rid of biological and chemical weapons would add moral strength to such efforts, 5. encouraging regional peace processes, particularly a just solution to the Israeli-Palestinian question 6. promoting human rights monitors, tribunals for violations and rewarding progress by allowing Iraq's reintegration into the international community and failing this nurturing democratic movements within Iraq supporting civil society opposition to Saddam through nonviolent regional and international non-governmental organizations.

EPIDEMIOLOGY IN INTERNATIONAL AFFAIRS

No randomized trials are conducted in international affairs, but epidemiology can be quite useful in improving decision-making in that sector. Randomization and blinding would be difficult if not impossible, for most environmental exposures on humans and in any case, would contravene the Conventions of Nuremberg, Helsinki, Tokyo and Geneva, developed in response to the Second World War medical experimental crimes of the Nazis and the Japanese military government. Further, the ethical boundaries on experimentation, for instance on informed consent, increase as the proposed effects of the intervention increase, and become more uncertain.

Tragically, one of the best-conducted and most well resourced studies occurred on radiation victims after Hiroshima. The Life Span Study of 93,000 survivors and 27,000 unexposed individuals used *longitudinal cohort* and *case-control* designs to study the life-long health risks of cancer and radiation effects [37]. In 1962 Physicians for Social Responsibility projected Hiroshima's devastation and health effects to Boston, Massachusetts, estimating the impact of firestorm, blast wave and gale causing projectile debris on mortality, physical trauma, and the short-term and long-term radiation effects: 98 % of medical personnel would die within the central city; the entire U.S. would not have enough burn beds to deal with this one city's victims; environmental radiation would cause cancers years after an attack [38]. Leading medical voices were thus able to prove there could be no meaningful medical response to a nuclear war. International Physicians for the Prevention of Nuclear War (IPPNW) later demonstrated the likely effects of accidental nuclear war or a terrorist attack and using such data convinced the leadership in various countries of the merits of disarmament, winning the Nobel Peace Prize in 1985 [39].

Epidemiology has also been used to describe the nature of the small arms damage to health and possible interventions [40]. In the United States almost 30,000 people are killed each year with firearms, second only to motor vehicles as the most frequent cause of injury or death for 15-24 year olds. One innovative study design has been to compare geographically and demographically similar cities with differing prevalence of gun ownership: Seattle, USA (41%) vs. Vancouver, Canada (12%). During the study period, while robbery, home burglary, and aggravated assault rates were nearly comparable, rates of assault with firearms were 7.7 times higher and homicides involving firearms 4.8 times higher in Seattle than Vancouver [41]. Other work showed that households in the US with firearms are three times more likely to have suicides [42] and five times more likely to have homicides than those without firearms [43]. The lethality of handguns is far higher than other methods of homicide and suicide such as knives and ropes [44].

Even war itself may be studied with epidemiological methods. International Physicians for the Prevention of Nuclear War predicted prior to the Gulf War that the war would cause between 50,000 and 250,000 deaths in the first few months during and after the war [45, 46]. Iraq Body Count (IBC) has sought to count the dead directly since the war [47]. Immediately prior to the 2004 US election, at a time when IBC reported 10,000 direct deaths, a retrospective study by Johns Hopkins University, showed 100,000 excess deaths, with general mortality being 2.5 times greater than pre-war and violent death 58 times greater [48]. A follow-up study determined an excess mortality of 650,000 Iraqi casualties in the 40 months post-invasion [49].[5]

Using such data may help guide international affairs, to decide whether the risk of potential harms of a particular proposed intervention is worth its purported benefits.

---

5   This study of 1,849 homes in 47 randomly selected community clusters, documented 629 deaths among 12,801 household members over a 4.4 year period. Crude mortality rates (all ages) rose from 5.5 per 1000 to 13.2; violent deaths rose from pre 2003 war levels of 2% to 60 %; 78% of which occurred among adult males 15-59 years. Though Tony Blair claimed these claims were flawed without giving a rationale, scientists from the British government validated its methodology.

Chapter 6

FAULTY ASSUMPTIONS OF SCIENTISM

While such objective decision-making, if practiced consistently, might serve us well in medicine and international affairs, this often doesn't occur in the 'real world'.

FAULTY MODELS

Hormone replacement for post menopausal women was initially promoted for symptom relief, but was found to reduce osteoporosis and to have properties that might reduce risk factors for heart disease. At medical meetings throughout the 1990s, physicians were told that it was unethical and possibly fraught with medico-legal consequences to fail to recommend hormone replacement for all perimenopausal and post menopausal women. Some even conjectured that it could be good for "preventing" Alzheimer's disease. All this was before adequate randomized controlled trials had been done.

The Women's Health Initiative (WHI) randomized controlled trial and others, gave lie to many of these claims finding that hormone replacement increased breast cancer, stroke, early heart disease and even Alzheimer's- exactly the opposite to previous conjecture! [50][6]

---

[6] This was multicentre cohort study of 161,809 women between the ages of 50-79, of the use of estrogen and progestin in women who had a uterus. The study itself was difficult to fund because of the general perception of the benefits of hormone replacement therapy HRT. In July 2002 the 'estrogen with progesterone' component of the WHI study was stopped early because of a 26% relative increase in breast cancer. Later the estrogen only arm was stopped because of an increase in strokes. Hormone replacement also increased the number of cardiac events from 30 to 37 per 10,000 women years of use. Though HRT also increases blood clots (DVTs),

In the end it seems that such initial guidelines by expert bodies recommending hormone treatment to all, were not truly evidence-based, beginning as they did with a flawed pathophysiological model and overconfidence about observational evidence.

Let us look at our limited models with regard to our bones. Many have assumed that if bones are heavier or denser then they will be stronger. Taking one of the early agents intended to strengthen bones, sodium fluoride to increase bone density actually may make bones more fragile. Drugs for osteoporosis such as bisphosphonates will make the bones more brittle if used for too long, and may occasionally cause the jawbone to die (osteonecrosis) and rarely even result in oesophageal perforation, which has very high mortality. How about prevention measures for other problems? Recommendations to avoid sun because of skin cancer may actually increase the risk of osteoporosis because of a decrease in vitamin D. Now we find that proton pump inhibitors (PPIs), commonly used to suppress gastric acid production in the treatment of reflux oesphagitis, may interfere with calcium absorption through this decreased acid production and now are associated with increased hip fractures [51]. PPIs have also been linked to low serum Vitamin B12 levels which could cause neurological or blood disease.

Vitamin A and E, antioxidants, for the prevention of heart disease and lung cancer, were actually found to be neutral or slightly harmful for these diseases in high risk populations including smokers and those with higher exposure to asbestos [52, 53, 54, 55, 56].

What is responsible for such errors? Let's look at a few very basic methodological errors that are commonly overlooked in design and evaluation of trials.

RELIANCE ON SURROGATE INDICATORS

"A surrogate end-point of a clinical trial is a laboratory measurement or a physical sign used as a substitute for a clinically meaningful end-point that measures directly how a patient feels, functions or survives."

---

strokes, ovarian cancer and gallstones and uterine cancer if estrogen is unopposed (used without progesterone), it does appear to reduce colon cancer, slow bone mass loss, and help with menopausal symptoms. Some patients with severe menopausal symptoms may weigh the benefit of improving their quality of life as worth the calculated risk of possibly losing their life.

Changes induced by a therapy on a surrogate end-point in cardiology trials, such as suppression of ventricular arrhythmias or reduction in cholesterol level or blood pressure, are expected to reflect changes in a clinically meaningful endpoint. A surrogate is not just a correlate; the effect of the intervention on the surrogate end-point predicts the effect on the clinical outcome.

"Surrogate end points can be useful in phase 2 screening trials for identifying whether a new intervention is biologically active and for guiding decisions about whether the intervention is promising enough to justify a large definitive trial with clinically meaningful outcomes. In definitive phase 3 trials, except for rare circumstances in which the validity of the surrogate end point has already been rigorously established, the primary end point should be the true clinical outcome." [57]

Cardiac arrhythmias are a major source of mortality after a heart attack. Two decades ago, anti-arrhythmics such as encainide and flecainide were approved by the Food and Drug Administration (FDA) to suppress ventricular arrhythmias which could produce severe symptoms or be life threatening. More than 200 000 persons per year eventually took these drugs in the United States to reduce these ventricular arrhythmias. Unfortunately drugs do not just have one set of properties and other properties of these anti-arrhythmics meant they actually killed more people than they saved[7] [58, 59, 60].[8]

Recently one of the newest classes of diabetic medications the thiazolidinediones, which controls blood sugar quite well, has been found to have negative effects on heart failure and peripheral edema, and at least some member of this class on myocardial infarction [61], fractures and possibly macular edema. The increase rather than decrease in heart attacks was unexpected to many, as it did help control diabetes, one of the major risk factors for heart disease [62, 63, 64].

---

[7] The encainide flecainide trial was stopped when preliminary data 33 sudden deaths 56 total deaths occurred in patients taking either drug compared with only 9 (22 total in the matching placebo control group* final figures showed later 43 sudden deaths (63 total) in the intervention group and 16sudden (26 total) in control.

[8] A meta-analysis showed that a one-third reduction in the risk for ventricular tachycardia with lidocaine (another antiarrhythmic) was accompanied by a one-third increase in death rate. Quinidine, which had been used to maintain normal sinus rhythm after patients with atrial fibrillation (a different arrhythmia) had been converted to sinus rhythm, increased the mortality rate from 0.8% to 2.9%.

CHOLESTEROL AND EFFECTS NOT ON THE CAUSAL CHAIN

Surrogate indicators such as cholesterol levels are useful only if most of the effect on on the true clinical endpoint (e.g., morbidity or mortality) is mediated biologically through a change in the surrogate marker, or closely related to something else which actually achieves the desired outcome. Consequently there should be a strong biological link between the intervention, the surrogate and the true clinical endpoint. One of the earliest cholesterol lowering agents, clofibrate, lowered cholesterol beautifully but actually increased all cause mortality [65]. Niacin also known to decrease cholesterol levels, did not reduce total mortality in the highly powered 7-year CDP trial [66].

Simvastatin use however has been associated with decreased cholesterol levels and with a 25 to 30% reduction in total mortality in patients with angina pectoris or post MI [67]. Whether this reduction in mortality has a casual relation with the cholesterol lowering properties of simvastatin is unproven, and evaluating a treatment solely on that basis makes little sense.

Without clinical end points, such as total mortality, such drugs as fibrates and hormones could be in widespread use for their cholesterol-lowering effects.[9] Given the complex effects of each drug not just on blood vessels and not just mediated by LDL levels, even the findings of Framingham or intervention studies, do not support focusing on a 'target' LDL of 2.4 or 1.8 after a heart attack, let alone with healthy populations [68]. We don't really know if using these drugs on people with minimal elevations in cholesterol without established coronary artery disease where any positive effect may be minimal or whether the marginal benefit of increasing the dose of the statin actually benefits a population let alone an individual patient.[10] Lower cholesterol has also been associated with such

---

[9]   Gordon's meta-analysis. considering 50 randomized controlled trials of cholesterol-lowering interventions, including diet, fibrates, hormones, resins, and lovastatin, found an average reduction in cholesterol level of 10% and a reduction of death from coronary heart disease of 9%. Unfortunately, these cholesterol-lowering treatments as a group unintentionally increased the mortality rates associated with causes other than coronary heart disease by 24%. In these 50 trials, use of cholesterol-lowering agents actually led to a net 1% increase in overall mortality. Gordon DJ. Cholesterol lowering and total mortality. In: Rifkind BM, ed. *Contemporary Issues in Cholesterol Lowering: Clinical and Population Aspects.* New York: Marcel Dekker; 1994

[10]   De Lorgeril and Salen point out that most cardiac deaths for adults over 35 years of age were sudden cardiac deaths . The only indicator that seems to identify this group as being at risk is C-reactive protein (CRP) --- not LDL cholesterol levels or total cholesterol or any other lipid parameters. For women the risk indicators were diabetes or smoking while "blood cholesterol did not increase risk." Yet data (including an estimate from Merck) indicates there may be between 500,000 to 800,000 US women of childbearing age younger than 35 that the guidelines say are "at risk" because they have "high" cholesterol. de Lorgeril M and Salen P *Secondary*

conditions as Parkinson's disease [69]. Cerivastatin (Baycol), [70] a recent statin, was withdrawn from market because of a rare but serious illness involving muscle destruction called rhabdomyolysis, a property shared to a lesser degree by other statins.

HYPERTENSION AND USE OF WRONG END POINT

Epidemiologic evidence establishes hypertension as another risk factor for cardiovascular-related mortality. Those with lower blood pressures have lower rates of stroke and cardiovascular-related mortality [71]. One of the early large studies of treatment for hypertension, the Hypertension Detection and Follow-up Program showed a 17% relative reduction in total mortality in patients with mild hypertension who were managed with a stepped treatment program [72].

In the last couple of decades many different drugs were developed to treat hypertension in a primary prevention setting. Diuretics, which were found to reduce the stroke rate and had been around for years, were supplanted by scores of other (more expensive) drugs which reduced blood pressure, had good effects on cholesterol, on kidney function and on glucose tolerance, were cardio-selective, bio-available, lasted longer and improved other lab parameters. Most studies were not one to one comparisons with placebo or diuretics (this was considered unethical) and one end point they did not study was the effect on life expectancy. When this was finally chosen as an outcome measure, lo and behold, the ALLHAT trial [73] demonstrated that these earliest and cheapest anti-hypertensives were at least as, and often more, effective than these newer agents.

---

prevention of coronary heart disease by diet http://www.healthyeatingclub.com/APJCN/Volume14/vol14supp/fullArticles/deLorgeriltrial.pdf.
Clinical trial evidence arguably is lacking for the benefit of statin therapy in women of all ages and men greater than 70 without heart disease or diabetes. Even manufacturer-sponsored trials PROSPER and SPARCL found significant problems with statins. PROSPER found a 25% increase in the risk of cancer among people age 70-82 treated with a statin for 3.4 years (p=0.02) while the SPARCL study of more than 4,700 people who had recently had a stroke or TIA found Lipitor to be not much better than placebo at preventing strokes   While thrombotic strokes were reduced significantly, hemorrhagic strokes, were far more common in the Lipitor group with 55 cases, compared to 33 cases in the placebo group. While the authors reported a trend towards decreased cardiovascular mortality in a non statistically significant way, there was also a non statistically significant increase in cancer and all cause mortality. Welch K.M.A. et al. The Stroke Prevention by Aggressive Reduction in Cholesterol Levels (SPARCL) Investigators. High-dose atorvastatin after stroke or transient ischemic attack. *N Engl J Med.* 2006;355 (6) 549-559 Aug. 10, 2006.

The earliest Calcium Channel Blockers, used to treat hypertension and meant to decrease cardiovascular mortality, actually increased it [74, 75, 76]. Most were withdrawn from market, only to be replaced by longer acting ones and a second generation of related compounds. The favorable antihypertensive effects of such agents may be offset by other mechanisms of action that are unanticipated, and unrecognized and undiscovered for years.

CONFOUNDERS: CAUSATION VS. ASSOCIATION

Physicians must recognize the difference between causation and association: this difference is captured by the concept of 'confounders.' For example, people who ingest a lot of alcohol also have higher rates of squamous cell carcinoma of the head and neck. But, this is not because of the alcohol, at least not directly, but rather because of the increased rates of tobacco use in people who ingest a lot of alcohol. Therefore, in this case alcohol was not causal but was associated and smoking confounded this effect because it was associated both with the "risk factor" alcohol, and the outcome, head and neck cancer.

Chlamydia pneumoniae has been associated with atherosclerosis and heart disease, but thus far not found to be causative. Searches for agents of immunodeficiency and respiratory failure turned up dozens of associated organisms (and non-infectious entities) before HIV and SARS were identified. Similarly, people who drink a lot of coffee are more likely to be overweight, than those who don't and problems linked to obesity such as diabetes may appear linked to coffee. Indeed such reasoning is analogous to supposing that, because most people die in hospital beds, if hospital beds are reduced, then fewer people would die.

In the Nurses Health Study, those who took HRT were more likely to be more health conscious and lead a healthy lifestyle, which inadvertently created the erroneous impression that the HRT was the reason for better outcomes.

SCIENTISM GONE AMOK - THE POLYPILL

In what was hailed by *British Medical Journal* editor Richard Smith as the most important journal issue of the last half century, Nicholas Wald and Malcolm Law used extrapolations to describe a Polypill to prevent heart disease, composed of a statin for cholesterol, three antihypertensives (beta blocker, diuretic and ACE inhibitor), aspirin, and folic acid (to reduce homocysteine levels) which they predicted could prevent 90% of strokes and 80% of heart attacks [77], exclusive of lifestyle changes, vitamins or alternative medicines.

Current treatment guidelines recommend multiple drugs for the secondary prevention of cardiovascular disease. In the area of primary prevention, however, the value of such a pill would have to be clearly demonstrated, rather than simply assumed. As Srinath Reddy says, *"Without such evidence, advocacy for the polypill would be a mere leap of faith."* [78][11]

Australian GP Ralph Faggotter viewed these recommendations with justified skepticism. Looking at additive or multiplicative positive effects without looking at possible negative implications both additive and multiplicative and then extrapolating to those without heart disease, is ludicrous, Faggotter asks ironically,

"Imagine what could be achieved if they added a few more drugs to the mix. Along with the beta-blocker, they could add a little salbutamol and cortisone in case it caused asthma, and a little Viagra in case it caused impotence. Along with the aspirin they could add a little omeprazole in case it caused gastric bleeding. Along with the statin they could add a little codeine in case it caused aching muscles and a little Aricept in case it caused memory loss. "Along with the thiazide diuretic, they could add a little colchicine in case it caused gout. Along with the ACE inhibitor they could add a little cough mixture, in case it caused a cough. Some of these drugs, in combination, can stress the kidneys so a little EPO would help control any resultant renal anaemia." [79][12]

---

[11] The benefits in absolute numbers may not be as great as the authors' paper indicates even if all goes according to their extrapolations. Paul Rosch showed that for statins, the absolute risk reduction of cardiac events was 1.4% from 4.1 to 2.7% and the number needed to treat (NNT) was 71 for five years with some six percent side effects some possibly life threatening including a one percent increase in cancer risk which might persist well beyond the five year period. Rosch Paul J More on the Preposterous Polypill Panacea 2003 www.mercola.com/2003/aug/6/polypill.htm

[12] Perhaps a safer more natural tastier alternative to the Polypill is the Polymeal, Using data taken from the medical literature, the Framingham heart study and the Framingham offspring study the authors propose an evidence-based recipe included wine, fish, dark chocolate, fruits, vegetables, garlic, and almonds. Data assuming multiplicative correlations was used to model the benefits of the Polymeal in the general population from age 50 which was found to reduce cardiovascular disease events by 76%. For men it would increase life expectancy by 6.6 years, and years free from cardiovascular disease by 9.0 years. Franco Oscar H, Bonneux Luc, de Laet Chris, Peeters Anna, Steyerberg Ewout W, Mackenbach Johan P, The Polymeal: a more natural, safer, and probably tastier (than the Polypill) strategy to reduce cardiovascular disease by more than 75% *BMJ* 2004;329:1447-1450 (18 December), doi:10.1136/bmj.329.7480.1447.

Chapter 7

LIMITATIONS OF CONVENTIONAL MEDICAL DECISION-MAKING PROCESSES

Why have guidelines led us astray? Part of the answer is failure to understand the limitations of our methods.

LIMITATIONS OF GUIDELINES AND EBM

After critical appraisal of evidence from well–designed studies from trusted sources, physicians must either be open to changing established practice patterns or have well thought-out arguments that they are prepared to intelligently defend. In some sectors, failure to adhere to CPGs can result in legal liability and disciplinary action against physicians. Some fear that guidelines will be hijacked by purchasers, managers or governments to cut the costs of health care.

There are concerns of partiality and commercial interest influencing Clinical Practice Guidelines (CPGs), especially those based on specialty consensus opinions [80]. Cultural factors, or personal foibles, politicians or lobby groups all may influence CPGs. Clinical decisions must also be consistent with a patient's individual values and preferences.

But many physicians misinterpret the EBM as being restricted to, and synonymous with, RCTs. These clinicians defend the tools of EBM (RCTs, metaanalyses and systematic reviews, sometimes of questionable and biased design) with religious fervor, often failing to recognize its limitations and experience outside of RCTs. Such physicians also may take clinical practice guidelines or expert consensus as representing the best data available. To paraphrase Frank Zappa – *"Data is not information, information is not knowledge and knowledge is not wisdom."* [81] To some it appears that its language and tools have been taken over by people in power and misused to justify harmful practices that are the opposite of the principles of EBM [82, 83, 84].

Following dogma, or cookbook medicine is questionable ethically, impacts on physician autonomy, diminishes professional integrity, may compromise the physician-patient relationship and be sub-optimal in terms of quality of care – especially when arguably the cookbooks themselves, have been cooked up [85].

The founders of EBM assert that *"Evidence based medicine is not "cookbook" medicine..... External clinical evidence can inform, but can never replace, individual clinical expertise, and it is this expertise that decides whether the external evidence applies to the individual patient at all and, if so, how it should be integrated into a clinical decision."* [86]

LIMITATIONS OF EPIDEMIOLOGICAL METHODS

Randomized Controlled Trials (RCTs) are a useful tool limited to answering very specific questions within a clearly-defined framework or context and taking into account those things that are measured.

> 'Deliberately, and of necessity, it (an RCT) focuses on one tiny little piece of nature to the exclusion of all else. It doesn't look at underlying structural causes for problems, e.g., it may link poverty with ill-health but doesn't look at why poverty exists in the first place. RCTs cannot answer historical questions such as why the incidence of autism or attention deficit disorder has increased. Most social or philosophical questions; what is important in life, what is right and wrong what we should value and why, are not answered by epidemiology. Studies can tell us what we are but not who we are. Such broader philosophical decisions should not be left in the hands of scientists, the medical profession, the drug companies or any other particular group of 'stake-holders' but should be decided by society as a whole through the process of informed debate in a participatory democracy.' [87]

Many of the problems of RCTs stem from the fact that it usually is the company which owns the drug which is conducts and funds trial. [88] This seems analogous to asking parents to mark their own child's exam paper and then expecting an unbiased outcome! Yet surprisingly, this does not seem to particuarly bother many in the medical profession or regulators as they feel enough safeguards are in place.

Published RCT studies may not be representative of the array of studies that are completed on a given topic (published and unpublished) because journals or funders with conflicts of interest may preferentially select for publication, studies with desired conclusions. (i.e., publication bias). To reduce this problem, since 2004 the International Committee of Medical Journal Editors including most major medical journals, has a policy of refusing to publish clinical trial results if the trial was not recorded publicly at its outset. However even with registration, we still cannot expect the literature to be balanced. We know that those trials with positive outcomes or something new, are still more likely to be published.

Trials are often carefully designed to have just sufficient power to detect predefined significant clinical effect but often without sufficient power to pick up rare but serious adverse effects. This may be because of budget constraints. However safety problems, such side effects as the proarrythmic effect of cisapride, often only come to light much later as the RCT duration was too short. Consequently as a minimum it is important to have our regulatory bodies require extensive post marketing surveillance as part of the requirements for licensing any new drug. But there are many limitations to purely observational studies to evaluate adverse effects of treatment [89].

Studies are often designed with power to show how a drug may influence an "intermediate/surrogate endpoint" such as a test result (blood pressure, tumor size, glucose, or cholesterol levels), or even a clinical endpoint such as number of heart attacks, without having the power to show that it decreases overall mortality in a population or, considering side effects, has a net positive effect for the patient population.

While empirically scientific understanding of the pathophysiology of disease may be valuable in initiating effective treatment, we can be led down the wrong path when we don't understand complex systems and our own limitations in performing science correctly. Statistical methods such as multivariate regression models to evaluate associations still have major limitations as prognostic tools. [90]

When occasionally a positive, meaningful result is found, clinicians, drug companies and the Media often assume these findings might be generalized to wider populations. Trials often fail to account for differences in gender, ethnicity and individual susceptibility including genetic polymorphism.

Another major limitation of clinical trials is their generalizability to many patients seen in an average practice. Internal coherence of data is important but we must remember that for many trials, less than 10% of screened patients meet entrance selection criteria because of factors such as comorbidities, poor prognosis, etc. [91]. Though patients are often excluded from studies for good reasons and we can know little about effects on populations not studied. While better in terms of research interpretation, such studies with restricted populations have less generalizable findings. Unfortunately therapeutic decisions in practice still need to be made on real life patients with complex problems and the results of many clinical trials cannot be directly extrapolated to these patients.

The more complex patient populations (more severe conditions, co-moribidities, multiple drugs) in the study, the more difficult it is to assess the treatment effects (i.e., treatment mean - control group mean), relative to the random variation (within group variation of both the treatment and control groups). We are less able to detect real differences for a given sample size.

The number of patients who would need to be treated (the NNT) for one patient to benefit (given patients with the same initial level of risk, treated for the same length of time with the same follow-up) is often a useful number. Even if statistically significant differences are found with treatment, with a large "number needed to treat", use of a treatment may not be in the best interest of individuals or the population, especially if a treatment is associated with significant harms relative to benefits (iatrogenic side effects, labeling, high cost, etc.). Rarely are numbers needed to harm recorded. Evidence may need to be supplemented with data from longitudinal cohort studies, registries, case reports, and post-marketing surveillance to capture rare or delayed adverse events.

For environmental exposures, studies such as RCTs usually can't be conducted for ethical reasons and those guarding public safety are forced to rely on lesser methods. Studies of pesticides are often conducted by industry itself using a single chemical exposure on other animal models. Regulators then employ a standardized, but scientifically unproven product safety factor — a fudge factor, meant to provide for differences between animals and people, and between different types of people (gender, age etc.) but in reality these may not adequately model real world exposure with multiple exposures, interactions and the effects of genetic pleomorphism.

Ecological studies are indirect – relying on limiting factors such as type of crop or job description and may have no true control group. Case Control studies may be flawed due to recall bias, low participation and loss to follow-up. However, for rare diseases or those with complex etiology, ecological and case control studies often remain the best studies available [92].

LIMITATIONS OF PREVENTION IN MEDICINE

But primary prevention activities should not automatically be endorsed. Even a theoretically effective public health measure such as immunization can have harm. Adding new vaccines to the immunization schedule especially with additional needles may not only increase childhood pain and reluctance to come into the office, but also the chance that parents may refuse all vaccines or forget to make appointments for some basic vaccines. And some vaccine efficacy relies heavily on herd immunity, e.g., to provide a substantial reduction in all cause mortality greater than 80% of the population needs to be effectively immunized. Such measures therefore could be counterproductive for public health.

A new vaccine against human papilloma virus (even if affordable, effective and not allowing problems later or selecting out non-covered serotypes[13]), could inadvertently increase adolescents' sense of invulnerability, increase the number of sexual partners they choose to have, decrease the frequency of PAP smears and condom use and ultimately increase the cervical cancer risk. The universal flu campaign in Ontario, Canada has not been shown to decrease the incidence of flu after five years [93].

As primordial and primary prevention are largely the field of public health so we will concentrate on secondary and tertiary prevention aspects.

LIMITATIONS OF SCREENING

Can there be harm from a test that is adequately sensitive and specific?

Direct damage from tests includes colonic perforation during screening sigmoidoscopy or fetal demise during amniocentesis to screen for congenital birth defects.

---

[13] Thus may have been a problem with other vaccines. 3 years after introduction of pneumococcal conjugate vaccine routine vaccination with heptavalent, overall invasive pneumococcal disease decreased 67% in Alaska Native children younger than 2 years (from 403.2 per 100,000 in 1995-2000 to 134.3 per 100,000 per year in 2001-2003, $P<.001$). between 2001-2003 and 2004-2006, 82% increase to 244.6/100,000 .($P=.02$). Non vaccine covered disease increased 140% while there was a 96% decrease in heptavalent vaccine serotype disease. Such an effect was not found in non–Native Alaska children who were less at risk years. Singleton Rosalyn J., Hennessy, Thomas W Bulkow, Lisa R Hammitt Laura L Zulz, Tammy Hurlburt Debby A Butler, Jay C. Rudolph, Karen Parkinson Alan, Invasive Pneumococcal Disease Caused by Nonvaccine Serotypes Among Alaska Native Children with High Levels of 7-Valent Pneumococcal Conjugate Vaccine Coverage JAMA 2007;297(16):1784-1792. April 25, 2007.

Important complications of the results of screening tests are the psychological effects of labeling. This is the damage done when we tell someone who feels well that they are sick. Historically children diagnosed with "heart murmurs" may have been "protected" with less physical activity and have been in danger of developing cardiac neurosis, portrayed, for example, in the film, 'The Secret Garden'. People found in workplace screening programs to be hypertensive, have increased work absenteeism, increased anxiety and other behavioral changes and even earn less, have worse self reported health status, regardless of whether their hypertension warranted treatment [94].

Routine electrocardiograms in an asymptomatic individual may work to the patient's disadvantage by consuming time and resources that could be devoted to possibly more effective interventions for preventing heart disease, such as counseling regarding smoking, dietary fat intake or exercise.

False positive test results may lead to unnecessary diagnostic work-up, interventions or treatment. Screening using unnecessary procedures such as electronic fetal monitoring may contribute to increasing the frequency of Caesarian sections [95]. Tests may cause unnecessary anxiety in the physician as well as the patient or lead to difficulty in obtaining life or health insurance. False positive results will be more common when screening for diseases that are relatively rare in populations. For this reason, and also that of resources, it is also at times appropriate to limit screening to populations with a higher prevalence of disease (high-risk groups such as Tay Sachs in Jews or colonoscopy in those with a family history of colon cancer) rather than screening general populations.

Currently, official bodies in Canada recommend that routine teaching of breast self-examination (BSE) be excluded from the periodic health examination for women of all ages as the manoeuvre hasn't been shown to increase survival and may cause unnecessary anxiety [96, 97]. Screening mammograms, at least in the general population under 50, may detect cancers early, but do not appear to save lives [98, 99, 100, 101]. They may cause psychological distress and result in unnecessary surgery, radiotherapy, chemotherapy, hormonal therapy [102, 103]. Advocates of annual breast cancer screening highlighted a 30% *relative* reduction in the risk of dying from breast cancer over a 10-year period, downplaying any risk of radiation, any pain or the fact that women having regular mammograms would have a 49% chance of being recalled for a biopsy [104] and little absolute change in mortality, even in the most positive studies. Radical mastectomy, the conventional treatment of choice for breast cancer forty years ago, caused terrible morbidity for patients.

The prostate specific antigen (PSA) blood test is somewhat effective at detecting cancer (along with digital rectal exam and trans-rectal ultrasound), but also does not appear to save lives when practised on the general population. Further, treatments which cause morbidity such as impotence and incontinence, may negate any benefits of early detection. For this reason the Canadian Task Force on the Period Health Examination, the Canadian Cancer Society, the U.S. Preventive Services Task Force and the National Cancer Institute in the United States do not recommend routine PSA testing [105, 106, 107].

Prostate intraepithelial neoplasia and ductal carcinoma in situ of the breast, virtually unknown before the advent of widespread screening, now account for a substantial portion of all diagnosed prostate and breast tumors and may only rarely progress to death. It is possible that over-diagnosis of dangers maybe the equivalent of false positives and partly explain why general population screening has not appeared to substantially change death rates from these two cancers.

After his own random, positive test for blood on urine dipstick done in the course of an effort to teach techniques to medical students, GP Chris Del Mar launched his own EBM oriented investigation of asymptomatic hematuria (blood in urine) finding little evidence that he would benefit from further investigation and treatment [108].[14] Consequently, del Mar chose not to pursue further investigation.

---

[14] A British study showed found 2.5% of more than 10 000 men screened randomly were positive for asymptomatic hematuria by dipstick testing. Of these 60% were investigated further by their general practitioners.

"Three had a serious condition that was amenable to cure, two had bladder cancer and one had reflux nephropathy. This study seemed to be fairly close to my ideal. It gave a prognosis of the outcome someone like me (my situation being similar to screening) would expect. " [I was] *"unlikely to have a serious condition that was amenable to cure. Of course, even this may be an overestimate of the benefits of screening. Perhaps those three people would have developed symptoms such as frank haematuria or dysuria sufficiently early to negate the beneficial effect of screening on their prognosis. "*

"Another study was done in California. Over 20 000 middle aged people were screened by dipstick for haematuria. An unexpected positive result was found in nearly 3%, 99% of whom were followed up. Over the next three years, three patients developed urological cancers (two prostatic and one bladder). This study is more relevant because it looked at the outcome of people whose dipstick test was not positive; their probability of developing urological cancer was no less than that of people whose dipstick test was positive. According to this study, the likelihood of my developing urological cancer was 0.5%, whether I had haematuria or not. "

How about diabetes?

After diagnosis, tight control of diabetes likely reduces the risk for blindness and end-stage renal disease (ESRD), and aggressive control of hypertension, lipid therapy, and aspirin use seems to reduce cardiovascular events,. As such many felt that early detection in the asymptomatic preclinical phase and earlier tighter control to prevent diabetic complications such as retinopathy and nephropathy would be of even greater value. However, the US *Preventive Services Task Force* found that *"additional benefit of initiating tight glycemic control during the preclinical phase is uncertain but probably small."*[15]

SCREENING FOR LUNG CANCER

Each year in the US lung cancer will be diagnosed in an estimated 164,100 people and claim 156,900. Screening for lung cancer using frequent, routine, conventional chest X rays has been known to be useless or possibly even harmful since the mid 1980s, even in high risk group such as smokers. The Mayo Lung Project [109] showed such findings to hold even after tracking patients for 20 years [110].

Hopes for screening as better imaging became available soared after a *New England Journal of Medicine* study published last year [111].[16] The 10-year survival rate was 80 percent for those screened with spiral CT compared with conventional figures of 10 percent, presumably because they were diagnosed and treated earlier when the cancer was curable. Yet this was seemingly disputed by a

---

[15]   Even given the most optimistic assumptions, the number needed to screen (NNS) to prevent 1 case of blindness in one eye by tight glycemic control for 5 years is about 4,300. *"Until we have better evidence about its benefits, harms, and costs, the role of screening as a strategy to reduce the burden of suffering of diabetes will remain uncertain. Current evidence suggests that the benefits of screening are more likely to come from modification of CVD risk factors rather than from tight glycemic control."* Harris Russell; Donahue Katrina, Rathore; Saif S.; Frame Paul,; Woolf Steven H.; Lohr Kathleen N. Screening Adults for Type 2 Diabetes http://www.ahrq.gov/clinic/3rduspstf/diabscr/diabrev.htm
       Between 30 and 50 percent of people who receive a diagnosis of impaired glucose tolerance (IGT) will revert to normoglycemia. Studies have found that between 12.5 and 42 percent of men who were found to have diabetes on screening reverted to normoglycemia after 2.5 to 8 years. Diagnosing them with IGT, not only may be inconvenient and waste time but may subject them to harmful treatments. Stewart-Brown, Sarah Farmer Andrew Screening could seriously damage your health *Decisions to screen must take account of the social and psychological costs* BMJ 1997;314:533 (22 February) http://www.bmj.com/cgi/content/full/314/7080/533

[16]   Of 31,567 asymptomatic persons at risk for lung cancer screened using low-dose CT from 1993 through 2005, the investigators found 484 with lung cancer.

JAMA article this year, which had a higher detection rate, meaning that the population may have been even more at risk, but no change in terms of survival [112]. The *JAMA* [113] study was primarily funded by institutions such as Sloan-Kettering, Mayo as well as the National Cancer Institute, the Department of Defense, and several European government agencies. The NEJM study received support from General Electric, which makes CT scanners, and Eastman Kodak, which sells the film.

How do we interpret this information?[17] Even the earlier Mayo Clinic study with regular chest X rays had shown a doubling of the 10-year survival rate with screening without improving death rates. So cancers may rapidly or slowly progress to death, not progress at all, or even regress. Over-diagnosis drastically inflates survival statistics, even if mortality is unchanged.

Length bias is a systematic error as screening detects more individuals with more slowly developing, as opposed to rapidly progressive, disease. These individuals also will appear to do better, as their course will allow more opportunity to be found by screening, particularly if there is a long, pre-symptomatic phase. Lead time bias gives the perception of longer survival without altering the natural course of the disease as finding disease at an early stage, increases the time from detection to death. This is one of the reasons why mammography appears to be a more successful screening tool than it actually is.

Another bias to consider in evaluating screening tests without randomization and control groups include volunteer or referral bias means that people who choose healthier lifestyles are more likely to be attracted to a treatment arm (that seems to be why the nurses health study seemed to show an advantage to hormone replacement,

---

[17] The JAMA study followed 3,246 smokers or ex smokers (average smoking history 39 years) and finding 144 with lung cancer, 3 times as many as without screening and resulting in 10 times the number of surgeries. (The detection rate was higher than in the NEJM study because this study had older patients and longer follow-up.) 38 died from lung cancer — the same mortality rate expected for people of similar age and smoking history in the absence of screening.

People with positive screens get more procedures including bronchoscopy and CT-guided needle biopsy. with complications from these procedures include bleeding, infection, and discomfort. Depending on the size and location of the lesion, a thoracotomy, opening the chest to obtain a larger biopsy, may be recommended. The death rate from lung cancer surgery is 5 percent while 20 percent to 40 percent of people who have such surgery have serious complications, including heart attacks, pulmonary emboli, and pneumonia.

OTITIS MEDIA AND ANGIOPLASTY —
TWO EXAMPLES OF EARLY INTERVENTION

In the US and Britain, acute otitis media (AOM) is one of the most common reasons for children to visit a physician and to receive antibiotics. Nearly $5 billion is spent each year in the United States in managing AOM. By their first birthday, nearly two thirds of American children are diagnosed with at least one episode of AOM [114]. In the Netherlands however, physicians treat AOM in children symptomatically with analgesics and antipyretics and reserve antibiotics for those whose symptoms persist beyond 3 days. Trials in the late 1980s and early 1990s seemed to back up this approach with no increase in serious complications such as –mastoiditis and meningitis - and little effect on pain [115, 116, 117].[18]

Angioplasty or percutaneous coronary intervention (PCI) has been practiced increasingly in the last decade. In 2004, more than 1 million coronary stent procedures were performed in the United States, where approximately 85% of all PCI procedures are undertaken electively in patients with stable coronary artery disease. The COURAGE trial, a new randomized study compared the effect of adding PCI to what is assumed to be optimal medical therapy and lifestyle intervention (advice on diet, exercise and smoking cessation) [118] found that PCI

---

[18]   A Cochrane review (8 RCTs, n=2,287) assessed the effects of antibiotics versus placebo in children with AOM finding a 7% absolute reduction in the risk of pain, or NNT of 15 children to prevent one extra child from having pain after two to seven days. Also for every 17 children treated with antibiotics, one suffered an adverse effect (e.g. vomiting, diarrhoea, rash). O'Neill P, Roberts T, Stevenson CB. Acute otitis media. *Clinical Evidence.* September 2006. Accessed from www.clinicalevidence.com

Glasziou PP, Del Mar CB, Sanders SL, et al. Antibiotics for acute otitis media in children. *Cochrane Database of Systematic Reviews* 2004, Issue 1. Art. No.: CD000219. DOI: 10.1002/14651858.CD000219.pub2. Accessed from www.thecochranelibrary.com Another meta-analysis found few serious complications with the only case of mastoiditis in the antibiotic treatment group. Del Mar C, Glasziou P, Hayem M. Are antibiotics indicated as initial treatment for children with acute otitis media? A meta-analysis. *BMJ* 1997; 314: 1526-1529.

Dutch patients had similar outcomes at two months compared to seven other countries where antimicrobial therapy is virtually universal. Froom Jack, Culpepper Larry Jacobs Max DeMelker Ruut A Green Larry A, van Buchem Louk, Grob Paul Heeren Timothy Antimicrobials for acute otitis media? a review from the international primary care network *BMJ* 1997;315:98-102 (12 July) http://bmj.bmjjournals.com/cgi/content/full/315/7100/98.

Others have suggested that antibiotics may be beneficial in subgroups of patients, e.g. children under two years and those with fever or vomiting but even this has been questioned. Damoiseaux Roger A M J van Balen Frank A M, Hoes Arno W, Verheij Theo J M, de Melker Ruut A Primary care based randomised, double blind trial of amoxicillin versus placebo for acute otitis media in children aged under 2 years http://www.bmj.com/cgi/content/full/320/7231/ 350 *BMJ* 2000;320:350-354 (5 February).

did not reduce the risk of death, myocardial infarction, or other major cardiovascular events and only provided slight and temporary relief from chest pain.[19] This study was funded by the US Department of Veterans Affairs, the Medical Research Council of Canada and a host of drug companies, with stent makers refusing to participate in funding.

MASTERFUL INACTION – 'DON'T JUST DO SOMETHING, STAND THERE'

Sometimes when we talk of prevention, we are talking instead about early pre-emption. The urge to intervene in medicine is overwhelming. If it is 'broke' we must fix it. It is often true that, as Voltaire said, *"The art of medicine consists in amusing the patient while nature cures the disease."*

Time itself often heals. Studies show that de-briefing after major trauma to mitigate the effects of post traumatic stress disorder (PTSD) may make things worse [119, 120].

In my local hospital cleaning of umbilical cords with alcohol, as opposed to leaving them alone, was found to actually be harmful and the practice was stopped a decade ago. There are actually a whole host of interventions in child birth which were once universally practiced, but which have now been abandoned due to lack of evidence for their value, including routine pudendal shaves, enemas, stirrups, draping, masks, lying in the supine position during labor, frequent vaginal examinations, and regimented timed breast feeds [121]. Everything about the culture of childbirth is different to what it was 30 years ago, most often going back to nature.

Boils must be ripe to be lanced. 'Incidental' appendectomies, with cholecystectomies or any other intra-abdominal surgery, which were meant to reduce chances of major problems in the future, were actually found to be harmful

---

[19] Between 1999 and 2004 researchers randomized 2287 patients at 50 U.S. and Canadian centers, with myocardial ischemia and objective evidence of significant coronary artery disease), typically blockages in two arteries, but medically stable, and about 40 percent of whom had had a prior heart attack. Following patients for an average of 4.6 years, Heart-related hospitalization rates were similar for subgroups of smokers, diabetics, or older or sicker people.

in the elderly [122]. Such procedures actually reduced in frequency once insurers stopped paying for it [123].

Might there be similar analogies in International Affairs?

Chapter 8

SCIENTISM IN INTERNATIONAL AFFAIRS: THE FAILURES OF REALISM

Bruce Jentleson observed that US Foreign Policy decision-making has historically been guided by various forces termed the Four Ps: Peace, Power, Prosperity and Principles. [124] Realist Walter Mead represented this in the policies of four US historical leaders: Hamiltonian Commerce or Prosperity, Wilsonian Moral Principle, Jeffersonian Democratic System and Peace and Jacksonian Military Might or Power.

Mead observes a difference in American and European approaches to the world which he sees as inevitable given Europe's recent military weakness. (For Europeans) *"The United States is too unilateralist, too religious, too warlike, too laissez-faire, too fond of guns and the death penalty, and too addicted to simple solutions for complex problems.... When Jacksonian America does think about Europe, it sees what Sheriff Andy of Mayberry saw in Barney Fife—a scrawny, neurotic deputy whose good heart was overshadowed by bad judgment and vanity. The slow-talking, solid Andy tolerated Barney just fine, but he knew that Barney's self-importance would get him into one humiliating scrape after another."* [125]

Robert Kagan puts this in terms of Americans being from Mars and Europeans from Venus [126], much as John Gray's popular *Men are from Mars, Women are from Venus* [127].

Both observers, while sympathetic to concerns about values and principles seem to see the 'Realist' approach, concentrating on use of 'hard power' and coercion as generally more successful. Is this true?

In international affairs preemption is also often cited to justify intervention. We are also told that we should not be Chamberlains. Yet not every bad actor, 'madman', or tyrant is a Hitler who has to be stopped before he launches World War III and the next Holocaust. The US national security strategy (NSS) of forward defence, not waiting until the terrorist attack, seemed, on the surface, to be logical. The pre-emptive battle against Saddam Hussein and the threat of his alleged weapons of mass destruction before he got too strong is not proving to be the greatest poster child for preemption. Was this a false positive diagnosis in a 'test' which is too sensitive?! Doing nothing in Iraq may actually have been far preferable to intervening.

Those who suggest alternatives to war are pooh-poohed as naïve appeasers. But it is often the 'Realists' who are being naïve. Even Plato's *Republic* described the cycle of governments from autocracy to tyranny then to democracy as a natural cycle of events likely driven by human motivation and the natural human desire for autonomy and self-determination. Consequently it is natural to think that tyrants such as Saddam Hussein would eventually fall to a democratic organization through natural forces alone. We must remember that most dictators, Latin American military ones, Southeast Asian, African and even western and European ones, including such unseemly characters as Marcos, Milosevic and Suharto, were overthrown not by outside military intervention or even internal coups, but by popular and largely peaceful, civilian movements. Resultant governments tend to be more stable than those which achieve power through violent means- violence begets violence. With military intervention, legitimacy is seen to come from military power rather than popular assent, possibly leading to further opposition, military despotism and then further military coups. Sometimes with preemption, the operation might be a success "Mission accomplished" proclaimed a banner behind George Bush shortly after the end of this Gulf War ...but the patient dies.

Peter Bergen and Paul Cruickshank attempted to measure the 'Iraq effect' on global terrorism [128].[20] The report also points out that the US administration's

---

20   *"Our study shows that the Iraq war has generated a stunning increase in the yearly rate of fatal jihadist attacks, amounting to literally hundreds of additional terrorist attacks... The study compared the period between 11 September 2001 and the invasion of Iraq with the period since the invasion began in March 2003. The count -- excluding the Arab-Israel conflict -- shows the number of deaths due to terrorism rose from 729 to 5,420. As well as strikes in Europe, attacks have also increased in Chechnya and Kashmir since the invasion."*

own National Intelligence Estimate on 'Trends in Global Terrorism: Implications for the United States' – partially declassified last October – stated that "the Iraq war has become the 'cause célèbre' for jihadists ... and is shaping a new generation of terrorist leaders and operatives."

Chapter 9

SUBJECTIVITY IN DECISION-MAKING

Assuming we are willing and able to make purely rational decisions, *should* we assess risk and benefits of our actions and inactions objectively? Sometimes values and morals render certain choices unacceptable regardless of evidence of, for example, economic or security benefits. For many, these include such issues as slavery, torture, committing genocide, capital punishment, and for some, reproductive choices for women or rights of the unborn. Decision-making in medicine, public policy, environmental and military affairs must be based not only on evidence but also on personal, cultural and philosophical values.

A rational decision to one person may appear quite different to someone else presented with the same problem. It is often important to be subjective, to let our own internal and external realities influence health decisions. Ideology though, is usually considered an undesirable influence, especially if imposed by with different beliefs or if it colors our perceptions of objective effects, and should be considered to reduce the adverse influences.

A physician who is a Jehovah's Witness may perceive the risks of transfusion as being greater and the benefits being less than those without such faith.[21] Not only may some on the US political Right still be searching for Saddam's weapons of mass destruction and his connections with Al Qaeda, but they genuinely may believe that the Iraqi people are better off with military intervention. Similarly people who categorically reject a military response may not realize that they condemn target populations to death by not intervening in Sierra Leone, Rwanda,

---

21   Interestingly it was concerns of Witnesses and blood contamination with HIV, Hepatitis B and C, that made it evident that we did not have to treat everyone with Hb under 100 (10 in US Units) and to realize that 'anemia' of pregnancy might have some physiological advantages.

East Timor or Darfur and perhaps may ultimately in the longer term, be putting themselves and their own societies at risk [129].

The political environment in decision-making determines what is possible and is most resilient with broad public consultation. In some cases the political system limits free choice and does not support public consultation. Sometimes the situation is not conducive for the ideal solution, and a harm reduction approach is preferred. This may include issues such as graft or child labor in certain developing countries or resource poor environments.

The problem is when we fail to recognize assumptions behind action and inaction such as devaluing the disempowered. When we delude ourselves and others into believing that we are acting objectively in such cases, we may inadvertently harm our own interests and those of others.

Personality traits and cognitive styles each may affect how we weigh risks to arrive at decisions. Behavioralist Isabel Briggs Myers (1962), believed that a person's decision making process depends to a significant degree on their cognitive style. Myers developed a set of four bi-polar dimensions, called the Myers-Briggs Type Indicator (MBTI). The terminal points on these dimensions are: *thinking* and *feeling*; *extroversion* and *introversion*; *judgment* and *perception*; and *sensing* and *intuition*. Other personality type issues may also affect decision-making. Some are more Type A; some cannot accept non- quantitative data and ignore data with uncertainty. Some think more concretely or in absolutist, black and white terms.

In health communication, people are known to have particular cognitive styles of receiving new health information for such problems as heart disease and cancer. 'Blunters' avoid information to cope with stress while 'monitors' seek information. Some physicians and patients avoid detail while others seek and find comfort in numbers, even irrelevant ones when challenged with information that is technical, frightening, where there is disagreement among experts as to consequences and management. The same may be true for generals, politicians and civil servants.

When frightened, people may mistrust the evidence or the messenger, considering them to be devious, cunning or duplicitous and display hostility towards the source, seeing no need to systematically evaluate such information. 9/11 conspiracy theorists find the US government capable of mass murder and able to keep thousands of accomplices silent but at the same time, unable to fake evidence for weapons of mass destruction in Iraq.

HUMAN ASSESSMENT OF RISK

In the US, the probability of dying in a motor vehicle accident in a year is 1/6500 of being struck by lightning [130], 1/400,000 of dying from West Nile virus, 1 in 2,000,000, and of a snake-bite 1/145,000,000 [131]. Yet in the public's perception the risk of a snakebite or West Nile may seem greater than either being struck by lightning or dying in a motor vehicle accident.

We often assess our own capabilities as being greater than others. 80 percent of us assert that we are better than average drivers and a similar proportion believe we are smarter, more attractive, and more talented than average [132].

Jim Holt and Trisha Greenhalgh [133, 134] each suggest cognitive and social influences that may prevent us from making fully objective decisions. I will separate them into the Who, What, Where, When, Why and How.

Who

People seem to value the lives of some greater than others[22] [135]. Those making judgments about others tend to be less risk averse than those making

---

[22] Tom Englehart shows that average award to relatives of victims of 9/11 was $1.8 million-thanks to the September 11th Victim Compensation Fund. http://www.cbsnews.com/stories/2004/01/16/ national/main593715.shtml This was consistent with court appointed costs for lost income.

However, in Jalalabad, Afghanistan in what was found to be deliberate acts of retaliation or admitted "excessive force" murdering "12 people -- including a 4-year-old girl, a 1-year-old boy and three elderly villagers" -- and wounded 34. After much protest in Afghanistan, according to David S. Cloud of the New York Times http://www.nytimes.com/2007/05/09/world/asia/09afghan.html, US Col. John Nicholson, a brigade commander, met with the families of the (now) 19 Afghans who had been killed and the 50 who had been wounded by the Marines. He offered this official apology: "I stand before you today, deeply, deeply ashamed and terribly sorry that Americans have killed and wounded innocent Afghan people." The families were given approximately $2,000 per death in "condolence payments" to family.

And in Iraq in 2005, through a American Civil Liberties Association Freedom of Information Act request, it was found that the value of life was similar, averaging about $2,500 per acknowledged wrongful death.. "ACLU Releases Files on Civilian Casualties in Afghanistan and Iraq," http://www.aclu.org/natsec/foia/29316prs20070412.html "ACLU Releases Files on Civilian Casualties in Afghanistan and Iraq," Greg Mitchell offered this description: "What price (when we do pay) do we place on the life of a 9-year-old boy, shot by one of our soldiers who mistook his book bag for a bomb satchel? Would you believe $500? And when we shoot an Iraqi journalist on a bridge we shell out $2,500 to his widow -- but why not the measly $5,000 she had requested?" Mitchell Greg "Sorry We Shot Your Kid, But Here's $500." Editor & Publisher http://www.editorandpublisher.com/eandp/columns/pressingissues_display.jsp?vnu_content_id=1003571125

judgments about themselves or those with whom they identify. We are willing to accept more risks for people we don't know than we are for more than identifiable ones or those more vulnerable, such as pregnant women, children or future generations.

People in positions of power are more likely to risk the lives of the poor or people of other cultures. Decisions are made at the head offices of a multinational corporation are more likely to favor shareholders with whom they identify as opposed to anonymous workers in far off countries. In recent conflicts, militaries of western powers have been willing to risk very few casualties on their own sides-, often wanting zero risk. For example the US was forced to leave Somalia in 1993-94 after the loss of 18 soldiers.

Those of the underclass themselves, often take the same approach, perhaps for different reasons. In North America, many blacks, non-unionized workers and those in lower socio-economic groups, presumably with less to lose, are willing to take dangerous tasks just to keep their jobs. In Third World countries, children may find working to be the least negative, short-term, personal option, because of the immediate economic necessities and with the limited choices society offers, though at a long term cost of perpetual poverty,

What and Where

We find poorly understood and therefore frightening phenomena such as SARS or Ebola virus outbreaks or those with hidden, irreversible damage or those that occur after many years such as cancers to be less acceptable, even if such risks are known to be small. We have a preference for the status quo or usual practice. Most people are reluctant to change current behaviors, (such as starting or stopping a particular drug) even when we know we will be better off if we do change.

The unfamiliar or novel or 'far off' phenomena such as a hurricane or tsunami, may be perceived as riskier than chemical spills, which may be more familiar.

The families or spouses of two dozen innocent Iraqis slaughtered in another Marines-run-amok moment at Haditha also after an attack on a convoy of Humvees that wounded a Marine were also given the same amount. The $32million paid out for US acknowledged deaths leading to a figure of over 6,000 "incidents"

When

We value things in the here and now much more than in the future and insurers place a value on, for example, money and life saved, twice as much today as ten years in the future.

Why

We are more afraid of involuntary exposures, inescapable despite personal precautions. The 'Anthrax in the mail' scare in the USA post-9/11 caused more panic and probably prevented resources from being devoted to other security concerns. Some might say that random screening of shoes and toothpaste at airports may mean that other security needs are neglected.

How

We place different values on life lost depending on the mode of death or disability. When the Washington snipers were loose, the seven deaths from drive-by shootings did not even represent a blip on Washington's gun murder rate, though it received much press coverage and was the subject of much angst.

Framing

'The glass being half full' or 'half empty', or relative or absolute increase or decrease may change a response. Most people have not been introduced to the concepts of and really don't understand "relative risk", "absolute risk" and "odds ratio" [136]. People more likely to avoid a loss than get a gain Preference for cancer therapy is known to be affected by whether it is framed in terms of dying or survival [137].

Zero Risk

We really can't tell the difference in a meaningful way between miniscule risks such as 1/10,000 and 1/200,000; we may have different arbitrary acceptable risks for instance for behaviours such as smoking and lung cancer and vaccine complications. We value 'zero' risk although there is nothing like true zero risk; every activity entails some risk and even doing nothing has risks.) Attempting to reduce risk to zero, suppressing the risk-causing activity, ironically, often increases risk in another area. Preventing skin cancer by reducing sun exposure may lead to osteoporosis. Trying to reduce the risk of children being abducted to zero, results in them being kept inside and sedentary which leads to obesity and early death from heart disease.

PRIMED DECISION-MAKING

Interestingly though, some decisions which appear subjective may truly be based on objective criteria. In situations with time pressure, higher stakes, or increased ambiguities, experts use intuitive decision-making rather than structured approaches, following a recognition 'primed decision approach' to fit a set of indicators into the expert's experience and immediately arrive at a satisfactory course of action without weighing alternatives. This often leads to good decisions ... as Malcolm Gladwell explains in *Blink* using examples of experts in gambling, speed dating, tennis, military war games, the movies, malpractice suits, popular music, and predicting divorce, ... but also may lead to disaster [138]. Let us examine where we act against our own interests.

Chapter 10

COGNITIVE DISTORTIONS IN MEDICINE AND INTERNATIONAL AFFAIRS

OPERATING ON FAITH IN MEDICINE AND INTERNATIONAL AFFAIRS

Many physicians assume that newer technology will be safer and better; that each new blood pressure medication, cholesterol lowering agent or painkiller will be better than the last. New painkillers, the COX II inhibitors, rofecoxib (Vioxx) [139], and valdecoxib (Bextra) [140] which were meant to reduce the rate of gastric ulcers compared with other older NSAIDs, appeared to do so, but actually caused more heart attacks and strokes and needed to be withdrawn from the market.

Interestingly, more often than not, good effects are assumed to be class effects, but bad effects, individual. When rofecoxib and valdecoxib were considered to pose unnecessary risk, the other COX II inhibitors were not considered bad (or at least the manufacturers of Celebrex and Mobicox attempted to quarantine their drugs from the negative publicity surrounding Vioxx), and though first generation calcium channel blockers were considered to have negative cardiac effects, the second generation and longer acting ones were assumed not to have these but to have retained all of the good effects.

CHANGING THE RULES OF THE GAME

Sometimes we go further, changing the evidence directly to fit our assumptions.

Doctors note non-statistically significant trends to decreased cardiovascular mortality with cholesterol treatment but systematically ignore statistically significant increases in cancers, accidents, suicide or hemorrhagic strokes if they don't fit with our model.

Re-jigging the experiment occurs in the Military as it does in Medicine. When initial testing for missile defense failed, the US military 'doctored' the results by changing decoys and putting homing devices, wrapping their missiles in tin foil so they could get positive results. The same, all-too-human motivating factors apply whether we are talking about Vioxx or Star Wars. This also occurred before the Gulf War in US trials of a war on a 'hypothetical' country with features similar to Iraq[23] [141].

Each of these mistakes: assumptions that screening and pre-emption only could have benefits, failing to understand causal chains, uses of surrogate indicators, wrong end points, and mistaking association for causation each represented very basic failures of logic and decision-making. Some were expensive errors and all harmed patients in the medical examples; in international affairs our own foreign policy interests and populations were negatively affected. Why would this occur when we seem to have so many checks and balances in the

---

[23] In the summer of 2002 just prior to the war on Iraq US military carried on a $250m rehearsal using over 13,000 troops and computer simulation. Millennium Challenge 02 was a mock war against a fictitiously named Persian Gulf country that resembled Iraq run by a crazed but cunning megalomaniac. Retired Lieutenant General Paul Van Riper was in charge of the "Red Force" (simulating the enemy) against the "Blue Force" (the United States). The "control group", the officers refereeing the exercise, informed him that US electronic warfare planes had zapped his expensive microwave communications systems.

"You're going to have to use cell phones and satellite phones now, they told me. I said no, no, no - we're going to use motorcycle messengers and make announcements from the mosques," Van Riper says. "But they refused to accept that we'd do anything they wouldn't do in the west." Van Riper was initially given a free hand using motorcycle messengers to transmit orders to Red troops, thereby eluding Blue's super-sophisticated eavesdropping technology, reckoned Blue would try to launch a surprise strike, in line with the administration's new pre-emptive doctrine, "so I decided I would attack first" and sank many of the Blue Forces' ships when they entered the Persian Gulf with suicide-bombers in speed boats.

"At that point, the managers stopped the game to "refloat" the Blue fleet, and resumed play. On several occasions the Red Force was directed not to use certain weapons systems against Blue, was forced to reveal the location of its units."

Eventually with such manoeuvres, the Blue team 'won'. The US now had 'proof' that it would win the war on Iraq.

system? The rest of the paper will look at why this might be so and how it might be remedied.

HEURISTICS

Why do many consider many of the harmful thoughts and actions to be scientific, legitimate, even "Realistic'? Heuristics refers to short cuts and rules of thumb we use to allow us to make quick, often efficient, judgments. They allow us to conserve cognitive energy and make sense of a complex world. We selectively filter any new information with prior knowledge, values, beliefs and emotions. We'll use heuristics when overloaded with information, when don't want to think about a problem, when stakes not important or when we have little or no information.

We rely on facts and material that are easily brought to mind, which may be overestimated in frequency or importance. Our recall is influenced by immediacy, strong emotions, and anything that increases memorability (such as press coverage and personal experience). An example might be concern about deaths due to shark attacks at the beach, when statistically far more people are killed by falling aircraft parts! Media and popular novels make shark attacks seem much more common than they are. Such *Availability bias* occurs in medicine when a doctor makes a decision, based on an experience that is at the forefront of her/his mind but which bears little relation to the patient being treated. We'll remember people apparently saved by early detection of cancers. Stories about the harmful effects of medicines have a particularly powerful impact on decision- making. When presented with a large amount of data we'll remember that which we first heard (Primacy) and last heard (Recency) better than the rest. Pharmaceutical representatives and TV advertising seek to keep evidence that they feel most relevant readily available to physicians and the public

With regard to our individual outcome or capabilities we may have an *Optimism bias*. This may also be because of a desire to be better than others or to shield ourselves from fear. With situations with which we have little personal experience, that which we think is controllable, that where we feel that early action can pre-empt a problem or that we see as very low probability this tendency is exaggerated. People engaging in the most unhealthy behaviours, such as smoking, drinking and street drug use, tend to be the most unreasonably optimistic about positive outcomes. In medicine, surgeons for example, generally feel that their success rate is far greater than statistics bear out. Groopman cites research that shows the worse the performance of radiologists, the more certain they seem to be that they are right! [142]

Representativeness bias occurs when we seek similar data to our experience but have an under reliance on direct observation. We look for a typical case similar to something we know, rather than relying on base rate information. An example might be a feeling that something must be better, because it is more expensive. Having relatives with cancer or heart disease or, in the case of physicians, patients with particular conditions, will colour our interpretation of symptoms such as chest pain.

We'll find a particular number, concept or value for a condition that we feel we understand and then relate to particular cases, adjusting up and down depending on our judgment perception or belief of risk relative to this number (*Anchoring and adjustment*). Media stories of breast cancer tend to focus on young cases, with the result that women in their 40s typically overestimate by more than 20-fold their chance of dying of breast cancer within a decade. They overestimate the risk reduction from screening by a factor of more than 100 [143].

CONFIRMATION BIAS

We seek evidence that proves beliefs; new evidence is made to fit while contrary evidence is devalued or filtered out. We ignore rationally constructed guidelines, considering the studies to be good but extend these conclusions to unproven, off label use. We even make the evidence fit our assumptions. "Diagnostic momentum" takes over when we are unable to change course, even though the basis for the initial diagnosis may have been unclear.

In the BMJ Jenny Doust and Chris Del Mar examined reasons why physicians use ineffective or harmful treatments [144]. Many of these represented a confirmation bias. These included: Clinical experience (e.g., arrhythmia suppression), Failure to Understand the Natural history of the illness (which might include the example of antibiotic treatment of otitis media), Love of the pathophysiological model (that is wrong which would include many of the examples described such as positioning of children to avoid aspiration and breast milk jaundice, Ritual and mystique (a belief in technological progress- stents, spiral CT for lung cancer, mammograms) No one asks the question or right question (hypertension HRT treatments), and Patients' expectations (real or assumed). All of these may explain errors in our attitudes towards screening for hypertension, cholesterol, and diabetes.

Sometimes we may have excessive confidence or trust in numbers, in experts, or in technology and therefore fail to ask critical questions. We recognize anti-depressants as helping with mood but dismiss agitation and possible increase in suicide risk. Even when we find things such as a reduction in breast cancer incidence or mortality researchers in Canada looked to mammograms as the cause for this reduction, rather than seeing the temporal association between reduction of hormone replacement therapy.[24]

Confirmation bias is found frequently in international and domestic political affairs. With the murder of 32 at Virginia Tech or earlier with 12 at Columbine High School, some derived a lesson that more guns needed to be available so people could 'take out' the shooter early, rather than seeing the solution as taking guns out of the hands of people, at least with mental health histories. Now, despite enormous spending the weakness of US military efforts and the attempt to impose 'simple' solutions is becoming evident. The willingness to 'doctor' the Millennium Challenge War game or Missile Defence results may reflect this trend. 'Why is it that people don't see failures of the hawks or of *Realism*?

Daniel Kahneman Nobel laureate in economics and Jonathan Renshon author of Why Leaders Choose War: The Psychology of Prevention (Westport: Praeger Security International, 2006) [145], looked at why hawks are so influential in political or military affairs despite lack of evidence. Hawks favor coercive action, are more willing to use military force and are overly reluctant to make necessary concessions. They believe that hostile regimes only understand the language of force and don't notice subtle openings for dialogue. They misjudge how adversaries perceive them, assuming that outside observers grasp the constraints on their own behavior, but they are unable to see constraints on others. Some might say that these are reflective of availability and representativeness biases. In war they suffer from an optimism bias, exaggerating their strengths; and they commonly overestimate their future success assuming relatively quick and easy victory. Leaders on both sides of a conflict often share such perceptions as with

---

24 Prescriptions for HRT decreased by 38 per cent in the year after publication of the WHI and they continue to fall. The incidence of breast cancer fell most precipitously, 11.8 per cent, in women aged 50-69, those most likely to take HRT. In the 70 and over age group, the rate went down 11.1 per cent. But in women under the age of 50, where HRT use was probably not a factor, the breast cancer rate rose slightly, by 1.3 per cent. The new research shows too that almost all the decline was accounted for by a drop in estrogen-receptor-positive tumours – those that would be most directly affected by use of HRT. However while use of HRT continued to decrease in 2004 there seemed to be no continued decrease in breast cancer. Ravdin Peter M Cronin, Kathleen A Howlader Nadia, Berg Christine D., Chlebowski Rowan T Feuer, Eric J. Edwards Brenda K. Berry Donald A The Decrease in Breast-Cancer Incidence in 2003 in the United States *NEJM* 356: (16) 1670-1674 April 19 2007 http://content.nejm.org/cgi/content/full/356/16/1670

the last Gulf War. Sometimes these assumptions make wars more likely to begin and more difficult to end. This may have produced the disaster of World War I.

From the point of view of much of the rest of the world, the US, far from being the practical, straight-talking, logical Sheriff Andy of Mayberry, actually exhibits many fallacies of logic.

Chapter 11

BOUNDED RATIONALITY

Bounded rationality, in Herbert Simon's words, means a variant of "rational choice that takes into account the cognitive limitations of the decision maker-- limitations of both knowledge and computational capacity" (Simon, 291). "Rather than consider all conceivable alternative courses of action, the boundedly rational actor conducts a limited search for a few alternative courses, often following standard operating procedures or incremental adaptation. She (sic) makes use of subjective beliefs, social norms, and cognitive shortcuts." Instead of optimizing, which is well beyond her computational capacity, she chooses "an alternative that meets or exceeds specified criteria, but that is not guaranteed to be either unique or in any sense the best" (Simon, 295) [146].

We are all 'bounded' in some measure, but may be able to expand our repertoire of making optimal decisions. Why do such findings of failures in medicine and international affairs not guide current practice? Why do they not enter the media or medical education? Is there effective control of information flow? Why do many Americans still trust their leadership and reject the opinion of experts about climate change as a phenomena and human influence on this process or if they accept it refuse to act on this information?

As with families of alcoholics denying issues related to alcohol, the elephant in the room that no one talks about, we have thus far not addressed two elephants distorting decision-making in medicine, environmental science and world affairs – the corporation and self-interest.

Chapter 12

DISTORTING DECISION-MAKING: THE TACTICS AND GOALS OF THE CORPORATION

THE GOALS OF THE CORPORATION

I do not wish to demonize everything about corporate or military structures and the people working for them. I have friends and family in each sector from the lowest to highest levels of leadership, almost invariably good thoughtful people; with a few other turns in my own life, I might also have been part of one of those sectors. Corporations and the military often are the least discriminatory parts of societies focused as they wish to be, on the bottom line. Racial prejudices, gender and class issues are often, though not always, less than in other sectors of society [147]. The medical technology sector and military have been responsible for advances that have been applied to other sectors of society saving countless lives. Militaries sometime deliver emergency aid, with efficiency not found in the government, developmental and NGO sectors.

Though most people working in the pharmaceutical, energy or arms industries may start out with reasonable intentions, the corrupting effects of the marketing imperative and the need to comply with corporate culture in order to survive and to succeed within the corporate world, result in any sense of need to present the facts honestly being subsumed beneath corporate interests.

The major goal of a corporation's marketing arm is to favorably highlight some of the real or imagined differences between its product and other competing products on the market. Some might say that effective marketing means clever manipulation of emotions-based behavior, convincing people, be they doctors, politicians or the general public, to make less rational decisions based on distorted evidence.

Social cognition is used by marketers. People are primed; events are made more recent. Decoys are used to shift reference points as in the real estate agent who shows a more expensive, but overvalued, house first. Sometimes they will use dilutional effects, flooding the environment with neutral or irrelevant information to reduce the impact of negative aspects of their product or to extinguish negative responses. Military PR people use the same tactics.

Marketing is often directed to generate negative emotions (fear, envy, shame self-doubt, anxiety) in people to make them feel inadequate or unhappy, (or that there is something missing in their lives- be it their health, their home, their clothes, in order to get them to consume. Satisfied, centred people, fulfilled by the simple things in life, are poor consumers. Advertisers must undermine feelings of contentedness to sell products. They sell the idea that health and happiness come through, and only through, the purchasing of products. Media-induced hypochondiasis is one facet of the more general issue of the discontents induced by the Consumer Culture.

A *British Medical Journal* study of advertising to physicians in the *BMJ* shows how industry uses the power of promotion and the power of visual and linguistic imagery to tap into deeper meanings from metaphors and ancient myths to depict exaggerated therapeutic efficacy [148].

As the magical Mirror of Erised in Harry Potter said "*I show not your face but your heart's desire.*"

MEDICINE-SELLING FEAR

Corporate-sponsored "disease awareness campaigns" typically urge potential consumers to consult their doctor for advice on specific medications. "Once the need has been established and created, then the product can be introduced to satisfy that need/desire," states Harry Cook in the "Practical Guide to Medical Education," published by the UK-based *Pharmaceutical Marketing* magazine [149].

In *Disease Mongering* [150], Lynn Payer described a confluence of interests of doctors, drug companies and media in exaggerating the severity of illness and the ability of drugs to "cure" them. "Since disease is such a fluid and political concept, the providers can essentially create their own demand by broadening the definitions of diseases in such a way as to include the greatest number of people, and by spinning out new diseases."

But can industry actually create a new disease? Andrew Malleson shows the evolution of a relatively rare and short term diagnosis of neck strain after a motor vehicle accident to the medico-legal diagnosis of whiplash where it now costs $13 billion to $18 billion annually in the United States [151].

Malleson does not deny that people suffer injury and a burden of disability, but attributes much of the growth in magnitude of the problem and the handicap produced to be due to the legal climate, to 'secondary gains' -- workers' compensation claims or lawsuits and noted the much poorer outcome of those with each. Of course some would say that people continue to suffer but not complain about things because no one is listening. He also shows how other illnesses such as "railway spine" and "repetitive strain injury" became rampant in other countries until laws allowing compensation were rescinded.

Ray Moynihan et al. illustrate tactics used by industry to make and to market a disease. These include medicalizing natural functions or personal or social problems as medical problems or ailments requiring medication such as finasteride (Propecia) for baldness or antidepressants for social phobia. Mild symptoms (irritable bowel, restless legs) are given the title syndrome with the implication they may be portents of serious disease. A major conference in Australia showed other aspects of disease mongering [152].

Risks factors such as osteoporosis or high blood pressure or cholesterol levels may be conceptualised as diseases in themselves [153]. Though the real diseases are fractures and cardiovascular problems, the drive by drug companies and individual investigators is to use surrogate endpoints in order to show efficacy rather than focusing on the real end points. There seems to be little alternative to medication to treating such risk factors.

Once the need for a new drug is established, Moynihan and Cassels show how industry may expand limited markets [154] to "persuade millions that they are sick [155]. Using the example of female sexual dysfunction, they demonstrate how science is co-opted.[25] Shortly after the introduction of Viagra industry began to promote it for this condition [156].

We are in a society trained to fear risk factors. Well, young people 'need' to know their cholesterol level, their bone density, PSA. They 'must' regularly perform home blood pressure monitoring without any evidence that this improves

---

[25] Though male erectile function is easy to measure, female sexual dysfunction has not been. This condition has been medicalized to a level that *"some clinicians now recommend, along with a physical and psychosocial examination, a comprehensive evaluation that can include the measurement of hormonal profiles, vaginal pH, and genital vibratory perception thresholds, as well as the use of ultrasonography to measure clitoral, labial, urethral, vaginal, and uterine*

their health. Medical journalist Alan Cassels reports that, even with an established disease such as diabetes, frequent monitoring of glucose may not be that helpful for non-insulin dependent diabetics.[26]

Citing statistics selectively and out of context, to maximize the size of a medical problems, advertising to patients to consult their doctors if they have certain risk factors for such conditions as osteopenia or andropause use of handy checklists for both doctor and patient, which seem to accentuate a perception of scientific certainty are all tactics used by the corporation. As the New York Times put it, if you have a pulse, you're sick [157].

ENVIRONMENT - THE MANUFACTURE OF UNCERTAINTY

The strategy of "manufacturing uncertainty" entails questioning the validity of scientific evidence on which the regulation is based. It has been used with great success by polluters and manufacturers of dangerous products to oppose public health and environmental regulation most notably by the tobacco industry, but also by producers of asbestos, benzene, beryllium, chromium, diesel exhaust, lead, plastics, and other hazardous products to avoid environmental and occupational health regulation [158].

Manufacturing uncertainty has become a business in itself; numerous technical consulting firms provide a service often called "product defense" or "litigation support" employing scientists for hire. The methods used by each industry - inventing an enemy, creating uncertainty - may at times appear reminiscent of the techniques of Nazi propagandist Joseph Goebbels.

David Michaels [159], Assistant Secretary of Energy in the US between 1998 and 2001 examined the operations of the tobacco (and energy) industries. Despite incontrovertible evidence from Doll and Hill of the association of smoking to lung cancer 50 years ago [160, 161], tobacco companies continued to throw doubt on lung cancer as being caused by smoking.[27]

---

blood flow. Industry has sponsored studies of "vaginal engorgement insufficiency and clitoral erectile insufficiency."

[26]   The Cochrane database of systematic reviews 2006, states there is *"... no valid randomized trial evidence that SMBG (self-monitoring of Blood Glucose) reduces either the number or severity of symptomatic episodes of hypoglycemia (or hyperglycemia)." "Getting people to test and retest their blood sugars did not improve peoples' quality of life, was expensive and even potentially harmful in that it increases patients' rates of depression, stress and worry."* http://commonground.ca/iss/0702187/cg187_chronic.shtml

[27]   They employed scientists who *"dissected every study, highlighted every question, magnified every flaw, cast every possible doubt every possible time. They also conjured their own studies*

The same tactic was used with climate change, with vested interests often demanding impossible levels of proof or creating spurious diversions to prevent governments from taking common-sense precautions. Legitimate debate about the extent of global warming or of the degree of human contribution, is meant to sow doubts about whether it is happening at all.[28] The approach is now so common that it is unusual for the science *not* to be challenged by an industry facing regulation. Short term financial interests triumph over the long term future of the human species and the planet.

And in the environmental sector, more so than the pharmaceutical industry, there is sometimes overt manipulation of evidence. Last year the International Journal of Occupational and Environmental Health had a special issue on "Corporate Corruption of Science" including issues such as asbestos, leaded gas and industry. In it the editors address issues involved with policy setting.

"Although occupational and environmental diseases are often viewed as isolated and unique failures of science, the government, or industry to protect the best interest of the public, they are in fact an outcome of a pervasive system of corporate priority setting, decision making, and influence. This system produces disease because political, economic, regulatory and ideological norms prioritize values of wealth and profit over human health and environmental well-being. Science is a key part of this system; there is a substantial tradition of manipulation of evidence, data, and analysis, ultimately designed to maintain favorable conditions for industry at both material and ideological levels." [162]

---

with questionable data and foregone conclusions. It was all a charade, of course, because the real science was incontrovertible. But the uncertainty campaign was effective; it delayed public health protections, and compensation for tobacco's victims, for decades." Michaels, David. The Art of 'Manufacturing Uncertainty' *LA Times* June 24, 2005 http://www.latimes.com/news/opinion/ commentary /la-oe-michaels24jun24,0,7062250

28 Frederick Seitz, a physicist who served as president of the US National Academy of Sciences became chair of a group called the Science and Environmental Policy Project more than twenty years later and circulated the Oregon Petition, which has been cited by many who claim that climate change is a myth. Arthur B Robinson, with no qualifications on climate science, and his associate leader of the Oregon Institute of Science and Medicine, became the lead author of the "review" that followed Seitz's letter. The petition was printed in the font and format of the Proceedings of the National Academy of Sciences, encouraging anyone with a university degree to sign as an expert. Soon after the petition was published, the National Academy of Sciences released this statement: *"The NAS Council would like to make it clear that this petition has nothing to do with the National Academy of Sciences and that the manuscript was not published in the Proceedings of the National Academy of Sciences or in any other peer-reviewed journal. The petition does not reflect the conclusions of expert reports of the Academy."*

INTERNATIONAL AFFAIRS — THE SEWING OF DOUBT AND THE MANUFACTURER OF WAR

Herman Goering said, "… the people can always be brought to the bidding of the leaders. That is easy. All you have to do is tell them they are being attacked and denounce the pacifists for lack of patriotism and exposing the country to danger. It works the same way in any country." [163] In George Orwell's '1984', governments maintain constant war with the enemy changing from one day to the next and people willingly following along, forgetting yesterday's friend as today's enemy and vice versa.[29]

It is natural for populations to wish to simplify the world around them; to demonize, to separate the self and other, the in-group to whom we feel some moral obligation and the outgroup to whom we have no obligation- and to view ourselves as just and the enemies, internal and external as unjust.[30] War propaganda tends to claim that only the enemy kills civilians, tortures POWs, and practices aggression and imperialism with the media, even in democracies suppressing all reports that "our boys" are committing similar atrocities to win a war. Lying, creating 'Saving Private Lynch' and 'Pat Tillman: Football hero turned war hero' fairy tales, only diminishes the reputations of the military.

---

[29] The movie 'Wag the Dog' featured the manufacture of a virtual war, by a PR consultant working for a fictitious US president, which only existed on the nation's TV screens, in order to distract attention from a sex scandal which was threatening to derail the president. This insightful and prescient film seemed to anticipate the war on Yugoslavia and the manufacture or 'sexing up' of the evidence of Saddam's WMDs in the US and Britain. Despite the oppression, major human rights violations and a refugee situation in Kosovo, these turned out to be comparatively 'mild symptoms' compared to the genocide or major ethnic cleansing that Clinton and Blair claimed was ongoing. A far greater case for war could have been made a few years earlier in Bosnia over Srebernica and other incidents of mass murder.

[30] Sam Keen's *"Faces of the Enemy"* Keen Sam Faces of the Enemy: Reflections of the Hostile Imagination San Francisco: Harper & Row, 1986.
political cartoons, posters and artwork showing depiction of the enemy in twentieth century war propaganda.
"In the beginning we create the enemy. Before the weapon comes the image. We think others to death and then invent the battle-axe or the ballistic missiles with which to actually kill them. Propaganda precedes technology."
Keen divides his illustrations into "archetypes of the hostile imagination." Including the Enemy as "Stranger", Aggressor," "Barbarian," "Criminal,", "Rapist," "Death," and Insect" One memorable cartoon panel illustrates tactics.
"Our enemies make nerve gas. So will we. They squander their wealth on armaments. So will we. They spy on their own citizens. So will we. They prevent their people from knowing what they do. So will we. We will not let our enemies impose their evil ways on us. We'll do it for them."

Jessica Lynch and the family of Army Ranger Tillman have shown true heroism in setting the record straight [164].

Not diminishing the importance or the reality of terrorist threats, today in the US we see pathologically heightened fears of packages of white powder in the mail, of running shoes, toothpaste and of young Muslims praying on planes, all accentuated by colour-coded alerts. Governments stockpile stores of Ciprofloxacin, to deal with bioterrorism as during the US anthrax scare, leading to shortage of supply which is picked up by the media and consumers who try even harder to get some for themselves exacerbating the shortage and panic. It is a well known human behavior to overreact to something currently in favour. This is well known in the arena of economic psychology where people race to pay any price for a commodity during a "boom" only to have a collapse in the price such as the Holland tulip frenzy of 1636-7 [165].

Doubt is sown and the onus of burden of proof reversed. Donald Rumsfeld asserted that *"Absence of evidence* (of Saddam Hussein's weapons of mass destruction or ties with Al Quaeda) *is not evidence of absence."* [166]

The lack of evidence of efficacy of medicine or procedure, (which have defined cost and morbidity) is met with an argument that there is no evidence that it isn't effective.

CO-OPTING DECISION-MAKERS — 'SELF INTEREST'

In domains of health and military security self interest or unconscious bias may colour judgment. Even doctors whom much of the public trusts as altruistic, may operate on self-interest or may view a patient through the limited lens of their specialties. Ear nose and throat surgeons once prescribed tonsillectomies routinely to all. When the evidence pointed to the lack of utility of such measures the number of tonsillectomies in the US plummeted from about one million per year to 250,000 over two decades. At the same time the ENTs discovered increasing merits in myringotomies or insertion of tympanostomy tubes (grommets) which increased by 250%. Consumer Reports found these and other surgeries including cataracts, cholecystectomies, hysterectomies, C-sections, and those for sleep apnoea and low back pain often unnecessary [167].

Radiologists and surgeons continue to recommend routine mammogram screening in some countries despite lack of evidence of benefit, especially below age 50, feeling that there are no harms and that we are developing better machines that will allow earlier detection and treatment that will be successful in the future.

Financial relationships among the pharmaceutical industry, scientific investigators, and academic institutions are widespread. Approximately one fourth of investigators have industry affiliations, and roughly two thirds of academic institutions hold equity in start-ups that sponsor research performed at the same institutions [168].

In Talking Back to Ritalin, Breggin describes how the mental health industry was going broke in the US in the 1970s with psychiatrists facing competition from psychologists, social workers, and family therapists. The DSM was revised to make diagnoses more objective and more medications became available to treat these conditions. An economic and political partnership with the drug companies in the 1980s allowed the profession to promote the medical model with drug company money through advertising in their journals, grants, special projects, massive support for professorships, lecture series and labs at medical schools.[31]

This also applies to other sectors. In the US the Department of Defence supports 37 percent of all federal research in the computer sciences and 44 percent of all engineering research, as well as significant shares of research in mathematics and oceanography [169]. The military industrial complex exerts major control in many societies with global defence spending now approaching $1 trillion US per year, about half of that taking place in the US [170]. Wars may be used to promote stagnant economies or to provide new sources of natural resources.

---

[31]   In *Psychiatric News*, psychiatrist Lester Shapiro (1991) identified the shared interests of the American Psychiatric Association and the drug companies:
"I am aware that the interrelationship of APA and the pharmaceutical industry is a complex one. We share research needs, appropriate product evaluation, planning for long-range goals, and the overarching considerations inherent in biopsychosocial patient care. It is far better that we engage in a serious examination and dialogue of the issues I have raised than to act in collusion with an industry whose goal is to increase drug usage by broadening indications for their drugs, advocating long-term administration, minimizing side effects, overstating effectiveness, de-emphasizing adjunctive treatments, or denigrating generic drugs"

Both the pharmaceutical and the arms industries have paid lobbyists in Washington, including former officials from Congress, or the government, think tanks, as well as the media. Both support candidates who vow to actively support their industries and provide jobs through favourable legislation, regulation and juicy contracts [171]. When it came to Reagan's Star Wars, contracts were given to companies in all 435 Congressional districts to give Congressional representatives a sense of at least short term benefits for their constituencies.

Chapter 13

DISTORTING DECISION-MAKING:
THE TOOLS OF THE CORPORATION

Think tanks, lobbyists, committees, consumer interest groups and news media are all employed to market the message of fear and uncertainty. Overloading with information, they attempt to distort our decision-making capacity.

COMMUNICATING THE MESSAGE:
EXPERTS AND THINK TANKS

To convince doctors, drug companies help set up boards of experts with key opinion leaders and launch a series of advertorials in leading medical magazines featuring interviews with members of the company's advisory board. These paid consultants also speak at rounds and various meetings, write or have articles ghost-written for them extolling the virtues of their product.

The Union of Concerned Scientists [172] produced a document showing how ExxonMobil used the tobacco industry's disinformation tactics, as well as some of the same organizations and personnel, to fund an array of front organizations or those which receive a substantial part of their revenue much as Big Tobacco had a few years earlier.[32]

---

[32] Think tanks such as the Cato Institute and the Heritage Foundation received money from bith Big Tobacco and Big Oil. Monbiot George The denial industry Tuesday September 19, 2006 http://environment.guardian.co.uk/print/0,,329579929-121568,00.html Exxon has been a major funder of climate change deniers including the George C Marshall Institute and the Center for the Study of Carbon Dioxide and Global Change. Greenpeace Exxonsecrets.org.

A national coalition intended to educate the media, public officials and the public about the dangers of 'junk science' [173] portrayed the danger of tobacco smoke as just one "unfounded fear" among others, such as concerns about pesticides and cell phones.[33]

In the 1950s, with the link between cigarette smoking and lung cancer becoming well established, the tobacco industry was in crisis. Its PR strategy, devised by the firm Hill and Knowlton, *was "entangling itself in the manipulation of fundamental scientific processes,"* [174]

"It was Hill and Knowlton's John Hill who "hit on the idea of creating an industry-sponsored research entity. Ultimately, he concluded, the best public relations approach was for the industry to become a major sponsor of medical research." This approach "implied that existing studies were inadequate or flawed," and made the tobacco industry "seem a committed participant in the scientific enterprise rather than a detractor." [175] The industry also created the "Tobacco Industry Research Committee."

Hill and Knowlton later became known for use of the 16 year old daughter of the Kuwaiti ambassador to the US in order to generate support for the first Gulf War. 'Nayirah' testified before Congress that she was a volunteer in a Kuwaiti hospital who had witnessed Iraqi soldiers throwing babies out of incubators,. Hill and Knowlton now does work for the nuclear power industry.

PR firms work on multiple issues. Burson Marsteller, like Hill and Knowlton, is owned by WPP, now the biggest communication firm in the world [176]. Burson Marsteller consults for clients including repressive regimes, Big Tobacco and biotech companies and against various environmental concerns [177].

PR consultants such as Patrick Moore, who left Greenpeace two decades ago has worked on a range of issues, where he has dismissed concerns about the impact of logging in the Amazon, supported Newmont Mining over controversies at its mines in the U.S., Ghana and Peru, defended the use of PVC in plastics and extolled the merits of genetically engineered crops. Since 2006 he has been a

---

[33] "Junk science" meant peer-reviewed studies showing that smoking was linked to cancer and other diseases. "Sound science" meant studies sponsored by the tobacco industry suggesting that the link was inconclusive. A memo from the tobacco company Brown and Williamson noted, "Doubt is our product since it is the best means of competing with the 'body of fact' that exists in the mind of the general public. It is also the means of establishing a controversy." Monbiot George The denial industry Tuesday September 19, 2006 http://environment.guardian. co.uk/print/0,,329579929-121568,00.html
JunkScience.com was founded by Big Tobacco but received money from companies such as Exxon.

consultant to the Nuclear Energy Institute's front group, the Clean and Safe Energy Coalition.

COMMUNICATING THE MESSAGE: ADVOCACY GROUPS

Teri Cox from Cox Communication Partners expressed enthusiasm about the benefits of funding patient advocacy groups in *Pharmaceutical Executive* Magazine asserts that *"Successful partnerships with third-party organizations such as patient and caregiver advocacy groups, professional associations, and thought leaders are powerful medicine for pharma companies."* [178]

"Industry-patient" partnerships, could "influence changes in health care policy and regulations to expand patient access to, and coverage for, earlier diagnoses and treatments ... recruit participants for clinical trials" and "speed the development and approval process for new therapies." *"Partnering with advocacy groups and thought leaders at major research institutions helps to defuse industry critics by delivering positive messages about the healthcare contributions of pharma companies."* Better still, an alliance with a non-profit group can deter inquisitive journalists. *"Without such allies, a skeptical journalist may see a company's messages as self-serving and describe them as such to their audiences."* [179]

What happens if no organization exists for your problem? To get out a "grassroots message" corporations' PR departments sometimes have created and funded front groups supposedly composed of ordinary citizens. Such practices are described by some critics and PR people as "astroturfing" — the practice of disguising an orchestrated campaign as a spontaneous upwelling of public opinion on a corporate message. In response to reports about the effects of passive smoking Big Tobacco began to create their own fake citizens' group, the Advancement of Sound Science Coalition to fight "over-regulation". Such groups manage to stay 'on message' but risk being publicly unmasked and leading to blowback for the company or coalition of companies:

More common and less risky in the pharmaceutical area is agreeing to fund existing organizations rather than to create their own.[34] Some older "patient

---

[34] According to the Union of Concerned Scientists, ExxonMobil funneled nearly $16 million between 1998 and 2005 to a network of 43 advocacy organizations that seek to confuse the public and delay action on global warming science. Oil Company Spent Nearly $16 Million to Fund Skeptic Groups, Create Confusion ExxonMobil Report Jan 3, 2007 Monbiot George The denial industry Tuesday September 19, 2006 http://environment.guardian.co.uk/print/0,, 329579929-121568,00.html.

groups" or disease groups (The Arthritis Society, founded in 1947, and the Canadian Diabetes Association, founded in 1953) began receiving funding from industry specifically to lobby and pressure governments on drug and health policy at a time when industry was less powerful and these groups remained more independent.

Sponsoring cash poor patient advocacy groups, supplying them with information (thereby filtering their marketing messages through organizations that tend to engender trust) helps medicalize issues. Some consumer health organizations are more than willing accomplices. The Canadian Cancer Society advertised that "Partnership with the Canadian Cancer Society can assist your company in reaching your commercial objectives" [180]. And the CCS is one of the best, having taken a courageous stand on hormone replacement. "Osteoporosis Australia, a medical foundation, which has received funding from pharmaceutical companies, issued a press release recently urging people to take a one minute test for their risk of osteoporosis. According to the foundation, *'we call this disease a silent thief: if you're not vigilant, it can sneak up on you and snatch your quality of life and your long-term health.'"* [181][35] Many other patient/consumer groups understanding such influences only decide to accept pharma funding after major internal debate and conflict.

Such tactics have been employed in the tobacco and energy sector. Communications firm APCO advised Philip Morris tobacco in forming the fake citizens' group: the Advancement of Sound Science Coalition. (TASSC) The chairman of Chesapeake Energy Corp, an Oklahoma City natural-gas-production company, set "Clean Sky Coalition [182, 183], running ads in *The Wall Street Journal*, the *Washington Post* headlined *'Face It, Coal Is Filthy.'* as well as on local buses and in the subway system, Some ads falsely claimed that Environmental Defense and the Sierra Club had "joined" the coalition. The ads were produced by Strategic Perception.

Both the tobacco and petroleum industries also sought to distance themselves from their own campaigns.

[35] *New Scientist,* in the largest survey to date of industry donations to patient groups, found only two of 29 US patient organizations, ruled out drug company funding. Most were reliant on them for over one-third of their budget. The Colorectal Cancer Coalition receives approximately 81% of its budget from drug companies. Marshall Jessica Aldhous Peter Swallowing the best advice? New Scientist 27 October 2006 issue 2575 pp18-22
Every group in our survey that received a high proportion of funding from industry denied that it biased their mission. Sharon Batt of Dalhousie University in Halifax, Canada, found that organizations that accept pharmaceutical funding "tend to advocate for faster review and availability of drugs, greater insurance coverage." Groups that maintain financial independence, on the other hand, "emphasize safety over speed".

REGULATORY BODIES

Close ties remain between regulatory bodies and the pharmaceutical industry the world over and industry is often seen as being the hand that feeds the regulator. In some countries, the regulator of an industry will be funded directly by payments from the industry it regulates — e.g., the Food and Drug Administration (FDA), in the USA, is funded directly by drug company fees. To some degree such relationships are necessary as people in the industry have some expertise but with cross-over in personnel, friendships and financial interdependence, regulators often see themselves as needing to correct public 'misconceptions' and 'fallacies' about their industrial friends.

In Britain, the Medicines and Healthcare products Regulatory Agency (MHRA) and the trade association of the industry it regulates, have engaged in drawing up blueprints for action and have done lobbying together. With the nuclear power and pesticide industries, with which I am most familiar, such considerations are often unconscious. The IAEA, meant to regulate nuclear power, is entrusted also with a mandatory obligation to promote nuclear power as a desirable source of energy[36] [184].

GOVERNMENT

If you have friends in government you can move the agenda further. A survey of 1,600 government scientists by the Union of Concerned Scientists found systemic tampering with the work of government climate scientists to eliminate politically inconvenient material about global warming. Nearly half (46%) of climate scientists at government agencies from NASA to the Environmental Protection Agency had been advised against using the terms "global warming" or "climate change" in speeches or in their reports. Forty-three percent of respondents said their published work had been revised in ways that altered the meaning of scientific findings [185].

---

[36] ARTICLE II: Objectives
The Agency shall seek to accelerate and enlarge the contribution of atomic energy to peace, health and prosperity throughout the world. It shall ensure, so far as it is able, that assistance provided by it or at its request or under its supervision or control is not used in such a way as to further any military purpose.
ARTICLE III: Functions
A. The Agency is authorized:
1. To encourage and assist research on, and development and practical application of, atomic energy for peaceful uses throughout the world; ...

In each sector, from medicine to military security, to the environment, the interested corporate sector has managed to sell fear and manufacture uncertainty to sell its product. Each employs think tanks or key opinion leaders, advocacy groups and influences regulatory bodies and governments to build markets for its product and to disturb rational decision-making.

Chapter 14

UNBOUNDING RATIONALITY: THE END OF SCIENTISTIC THINKING AND CORPORATE - MILITARY CONTROL OF DECISION-MAKING

"Stuff happens." But in terms of what's going on in that country, it is a fundamental misunderstanding to see those images over and over and over again of some boy walking out with a vase and say, "Oh, my goodness, you didn't have a plan' ... It's untidy, and freedom's untidy, and free people are free to make mistakes and commit crimes and do bad things. They're also free to live their lives and do wonderful things, and that's what's going to happen here." [186]

Quote from Donald Rumsfeld, former U.S. Secretary of Defense and architect of the war on Iraq

Stuff doesn't just happen. The effects of the Gulf War were predictable. In the worlds of medicine, environmental and international affairs, we are adrift, or worse, entirely on the wrong course. When current approaches don't seem to work, we must reverse gear and look at alternative approaches. In the Western World or Global North, supporting despotic oil regimes, continuing reckless oil consumption and pumping out greenhouse gases is not in our long-term interests.

The Health Belief Model [187] was developed by social psychologists in the 1950s after the failure of a free TB screening program by the US Public Health Service. It was found that individuals take health- related action if they believe that the severity of consequences is major, that the consequence can be avoided, there is positive expectation taking action will avoid consequences and that they can successfully undertake action (that they have the skills and confidence) to do so.

Albert Bandura, a father of Social Learning theory explained in 1977, that there has to be an expectation that change will have positive consequences, made an expectancy it that it has value and should be made, that an individual feels capable, that they can monitor progress and that there are positive reinforcers [188].

Public health physician John Last similarly describes social change occurring on public health problems when we are aware that the problem exists, know what causes the problem, believe that it is important, believe in our ability to control the cause and have the political will to make the changes [189].

Until recently physicians may not have believed that the system could change or that they have agency and most people, even in democracies, either do not believe that they can change the international system. I believe that the time is ripe for change in each of these sectors.

A NEED TO CHANGE: FAILURE OF CURRENT APPROACHES

To quote Dr. Rumsfeld again, *"There are known knowns. These are things we know that we know. There are known unknowns. That is to say, there are things that we know we don't know. But there are also unknown unknowns. There are things we don't know we don't know."* [190]

This paper has been largely designed to show problems in terms of scientism and corporate/military distortion in each of, the energy, environmental and international security. The problems are knowable and solutions too.

When we look at effectiveness what do we find? Policies that leave us somewhat less secure and unsustainable, increased terrorism, decreased resources, increased output of greenhouse gases and continuing to sell policies that all is OK if we'll just turn the other way. *"Of the seventy-eight drugs approved by the FDA in 2002, only seventeen contained new active ingredients, and only seven of these were classified by the FDA as improvements over older drugs."* [191] Just four new molecular entities (NMEs) were introduced in Europe and seven in the US in 2005" [192]. The benefits of medical action may not be as great as we hope nor the risks of medical inaction as great as we fear.

As Marcia Angell, former editor of the New England Journal of Medicine declared the pharmaceutical industry is "...extraordinarily privileged. It benefits from publicly funded research, government-granted patents and large tax breaks whilst it reaps lavish profits." [193] The same might be said for the oil and gas, auto, and nuclear power sectors and of course the military industries. Such failures should be invite closer scrutiny and a search for alternatives.

Failures in the pharmaceutical area are multiple. Decisions made in world affairs bear little relation to long term goals. Looking at smart bombs, guns, cluster munitions and nuclear weapons to achieve security in the short term may ultimately increase dangers. On nuclear weapons we have moved from policies parading the benefits of unilateral possession of nuclear weapons in the 1940s and 50s, to bilateral possession/detente (Mutually Assured Destruction) in the 70s and 80s to today's claims that they are beneficial for our friends and allies but need to be proscribed for others[37] [194].

We are looking at crises in terms of air quality, fossil fuel scarcity and climate change. Solutions such as the use of corn for ethanol which requires more energy to make than one gains are only profitable in the US because of farm subsidies, but do nothing to save energy.

It is the 'scientistic', as opposed to the scientific, approach that must be thrown out. A belief in scientific medicine for resolving empirical questions is not wrong. But what we often have now is attempting to answer non-empirical questions or answering the wrong question, a flawed belief in science for science's sake.

Pragmatism seeks to reconcile the competing philosophies of empiricism (concepts as inductive generalizations from sensory experience) and rationalism (concepts as mental phenomenon understood as prior to experience, thus conceiving of knowledge in deductive terms). Understanding the limitations of the 'scientistic' approach and judiciously applying it, knowing heuristics, cognitive distortions, how we mis-evaluate risk, making assumptions explicit, improving information flows and keeping information transparent, can only improve our decision-making [195].

---

[37] I said in a response to Charles Krauthammer's argument in an essay in *Time* magazine, entitled "The Terrible Logic of Nukes" that nuclear weapons protected the peace by maintaining a delicate balance of terror was that it *was just that: terrible logic. Iraq wants nuclear weapons to balance Israel's, which built them to balance Arab conventional superiority. Pakistan wanted to balance India, which had to balance China, which had to balance Russia, which had to balance the U.S. and its allies, which had to balance Russia's presumed European-theater superiority. Throughout this balancing act, the world has been no more than 30 minutes away from Armageddon. The only logical way to keep nuclear weapons out of the hands of madmen is to renounce them ourselves.*

BARRIERS TO CHANGE: THE MEDICO-PHARMA AND MILITARY-INDUSTRIAL COMPLEXES

I am convinced that in medicine, such errors represent a systemic and systematic failure in the system due, for example, to 1. inadequate initial and then post-marketing surveillance, 2. lack of transparency of studies, 3. drug company control of medical education, 4. lack of interest from the medical profession, 5. undue influence that business partnerships at times exert on the universities, 6. poor regulation and, 7. lack of political interest/will. Each of these has a parallel in environmental decision-making and international affairs where similar industrial, corporate and military control of agenda through research education, media and government is enabled by lack of interest or self-interest of decision-makers,

In medicine and international affairs, these distorted assumptions and values allow decision-makers with fiduciary responsibilities such as doctors and political representatives, consciously or unconsciously, to act against the interests of their constituents or patients. Ultimately this will undermine confidence in the whole process and will not serve the long-term interests even of these sectors, which see themselves as beneficiaries.

As Dwight Eisenhower warned in 1961 [196]

> This conjunction of an immense military establishment and a large arms industry is new in the American experience. The total influence -- economic, political, even spiritual – is felt in every city, every State house, every office of the Federal government. We recognize the imperative need for this development. Yet we must not fail to comprehend its grave implications. Our toil, resources and livelihood are all involved; so is the very structure of our society.

> In the councils of government, we must guard against the acquisition of unwarranted influence, whether sought or unsought, by the military-industrial complex. The potential for the disastrous rise of misplaced power exists and will persist.

James Madison warned in 1795, "Of all the enemies of public liberty, war is perhaps the most to be dreaded, because it comprises and develops the germ of every other." [197]

Both the pharmaceutical and military industries are considered sacrosanct in terms of legislation- accountable to the public neither in terms of budget, nor effectiveness. To ask real, meaningful or profound questions to do performance appraisals, may be perceived as unpatriotic, even dangerous. A culture of fear makes holistic, non-pharmacologic approaches to health and non-military approaches to security, seem less viable. The militaristic press and lobbyists tell us that a military response to conflict is the only one possible. Just as spokespeople from the pharmaceutical industry dominate the airwaves, a parade of military and ex-military analysts on US television before this last Gulf War monopolized the stage preparing the groundwork for 'war as the only alternative'.

Yes says the skeptic. *Defining the problem and solution is a theoretical exercise, in an ideal world in which a Plato-style philosopher-prince has to make public policy decisions. Looking at who is making the decision, what is their motivation, what is their desired outcome and why. What caused a particular decision to be made to achieve that outcome — what was the reasoning behind it? Was the reasoning sound? Were the putative reasons the real reasons or was there a hidden agenda? Will a decision help in the short-term but hinder in the long term? Who really made the decision for the US to go to war in Iraq not just who was the frontman? What were their motives? Who really gains from the implementation of the decision? Perhaps the ultimate decision-makers happy with results of Iraq or failure of drugs. Often the answer to this is complex - A cluster/cabal of self-interested parties will often have worked together to soften up the politicians, the public and professions to accept some new idea, which is supposedly in the interest of the public* [198].

But even if true, such thinking neglects the Decision-making power that is still within the control of individuals, especially in democracies.

Even people working in the pharmaceutical, energy and military sectors who are usually well-intentioned and thoughtful but don't see a way out and don't see themselves as decision-makers. They suffer from a sense of powerlessness or inertia and resign themselves to a default position of rationalism that they are doing the least harm or naked self interest professionally and splitting personally. What can increase the will to change?

WILL TO CHANGE

Human beings are among the most adaptable of species. Once our mind is made up to change this system, we are capable of major shifts. Rational changes inputs open processes better system in medicine and world affairs As such we can create the political will to change decision-making processes. Malcolm Gladwell shows that once societies reach the tipping point, they may be capable of rapid and productive change [199]. Former US Vice President Al Gore believes that democracies are capable of a rapid and effective response once they make up their minds to act. People have been able to effect great social change despite resistance of leaders from the abolition of slavery, to universal suffrage to the end of overt colonialism or in the health sector to attitudes towards smoking and drinking and driving.

James O Prochaska and Carlo Di Clemente studied the way in which people are able to make decisions to improve their health such as quitting smoking [200]. The stages of change model ranges from Pre-contemplation (with little awareness of a problem and no anticipation of change), to Contemplation (awareness of a problem but no effective plan) to Preparation (intent and a valid plan) to Action (where an attempt has been made to change) followed by Maintenance (> 6 months free of the harmful behavior). Collectively, with regard to changes in our way of decision-making in Medicine and International Affairs, we are in the 'pre-contemplation' stage.

How do we push to the action stage described by Prochaska and Di Clemente?

Looking at things psychotherapeutically we must look at the small changes we can make in our own behaviour and the first step solution-focused, when confronted with a problem. The above attitudes/ rationalizations against change of 'scientism' represent distortions pointed out by Aaron Beck [201], *All or nothing, Overgeneralization, Negative filter discounting the positive.* The main thing is to alter the decision-making balance for individuals and institutions to show on balance the pros of change outweigh cons.

People are often ahead of leaders on action related to issues such as Climate Change or, Third World Debt. They recognize the interdependence in this world and the need to change and are capable of changes. The medical system is also capable of change. Patients of all education levels and cultures are open to a dialogue on the relative merits and harms of interventions as well as uncertainties.

Militaries also saw no way to give up landmines, the cotton industry in the US to manage without slaves, Airlines and restaurants were unable to see their world without smoking, before such decisions were thrust upon them..

Recent events make the situation ripe to accept change. Intelligence 'sexed-up' or hyped in both the US and Britain prior to the last war may have undermined public confidence the next time either country tries to use information gained from secret sources to argue for war. The same might be said for the pharmaceutical industry, which has suffered repeated black eyes related to suppressed studies and the necessity for drug withdrawal. Such events lead to conflict with dearly held assumptions. 'Conflict' in Peace Studies, is seen as a situation with perceived incompatible goals but where there may be a chance to grow. This may be the time to make a change with balanced arguments and credible sources, allowing people to confirm or modify their opinions.

Negative behaviors by the US military including massacres of civilians at Jalalabad in March 2007 [202]. and Haditha in November 2005 [203], torture at Abu Ghraib and the cover-ups afterwards have increased the strength of the insurgency and undermined support for the war effort at home.[38]

The Boomerang effect when companies like Exxon Mobil, Merck or Pepsi use front groups make such tactics less attractive [204, 205, 206]. Spin of the Day and SourceWatch expose disinformation by various sources, their backing and affiliations.

We are now more skeptical as a public, being "inoculated," or forewarned about the presence of front groups presence. One study indicated "*that exposure, which reveals the corporate sponsors and true motives of corporate front-group stealth campaigns, backfires, not only against efforts to shape the attitude object but also against the image, reputation, credibility and citizenship assessments of front groups and their corporate sponsors. In short, there is significant risk associated with front-group stealth campaigns, which sponsors ignore at their peril*" [207].

One avenue of action used frequently in the US to fight back is the legal one-"Product Liability". Many class action drug cases have been successful. In the social realm class action suits are less frequent and more difficult.[39] Some are suing in US courts related to damage from the War on Terror involving torture but as yet attempts to impeach the President or to force the Prime Minister of Britain

---

38   In international and diplomatic negotiations, game theory which stemmed from research performed during world war II, has been used to quantitate the effect of certain decisions. In effect the best overall decision to make within a two party model in game theory is to return a good deed with another good deed. Models using an assumption of instigating a bad deed end up with another bad deed in return from the affected party.

39   *In the late 1990s, thousands of smokers from Florida brought a class action for the damage to their health against America's five biggest cigarette makers under the name of Howard Engle, an 86-year-old paediatrician with respiratory diseases and lymphoma. In 2000, a jury decided the tobacco companies should pay a punitive award of $145bn (£76bn). But the state's appeal court decided that Florida's smokers should not have been allowed to bring a class action. In 1998, New Orleans and Chicago sued gun-makers to force them to cover police and hospital costs incurred by their weapons, arguing that the firearms industry was liable because it made "unreasonably dangerous" products which lacked the safety mechanisms necessary to ensure only their owners could use them. In January 2003, the families of two men killed by the Washington snipers sued the shop where the suspects bought their high-powered rifle. California, sued the six largest carmakers in the US - Ford, General Motors, Toyota, Honda, Chrysler and Nissan - for allegedly creating a "public nuisance" costing it millions of dollars due to vehicle emissions and contributing to global warming.* Glaister Dan California sues car firms for global warming Green campaigners hail landmark action · Six largest manufacturers creating 'public nuisance' The Guardian Thursday September 21, 2006.

from office for their conduct on the war on Iraq and for launching it with false information have failed.

In the environmental sector though, regulators in both the pesticide and nuclear industries which I am involved with have become more cognisant of possible biases related to their relationship with industry in the last decade, perhaps in response to scandal or public pressure. Following the accidents at the Three Mile Island and Chernobyl reactors the regulatory requirements for nuclear power reactors all over the world has been upgraded. Also, many new reactor designs are much more robust than the previous reactors to deal with malevolent acts. The US Nuclear Regulatory Commission now tries to approach decision-making using probabilistic risk analysis [208]. It describes Principles of Good Regulation which include Independence, Openness, Efficiency, Clarity and Reliability while its Organizational Values include Integrity, Excellence, Service, Respect, Cooperation and Commitment.

Can we convince corporations and militaries not to use selling Fear or marketing Uncertainty as their primary modus operandi? Or can we persuade governments and medical practitioners or their tools not to participate? Or the public not to believe?

Prudent self-interest, an understanding of shared benefits and costs, a recognition of tradeoffs and internalization of costs can be used with work in international affairs or the pharmaceutical industry. For instance requiring manufacturers to either produce or give up patents on essential drugs to deal with diseases in the developing world, or to be taxed in some sort of global fund in order to be allowed to develop their products to governments manufacturing drugs themselves. Such products do not make much profit for manufacturers compared to those for chronic diseases in the West and as such no significant developments have taken place in the last thirty years.

With sitting stakeholders around the table, a broad spectrum of solutions might be explored. These might include taxes or voluntary payments (people in the North willing to pay a few cents extra on a bottle of tablets to deal with river blindness), highlighting the positive publicity from the marketplace with corporate generosity, much as the Gates foundation has done, to the promotion of generics.. With operant conditioning we might hope that positive results will reinforce the positive negative behaviours eventually become extinct.

Till recently on environmental issues, it has been the skeptics who are marginalized whose voices aren't heard as loudly in the mainstream media. But that is beginning to change.

Even PR firm Hill and Knowlton recognized a reason to change. Its Chairman and General Manager, Thomas Buckmaster. advises firms after a disaster to "Defusing Sensitive Issues Through 'Risk Communication,' "(1) Acknowledge the concerns of the other side; (2) Encourage joint fact-finding commissions; (3) Offer alternatives to minimize impacts; (4) Accept responsibilities, admit mistakes, and share power; (5) Focus on building long-term relationships; and (6) Act in what will be perceived as a trustworthy fashion" [209]. Buckmaster was not advocating changing tactics and truly partnering, but with corporations seeing exposure of activity, they are beginning to change.

In an apparent policy shift, earlier this year Exxon Mobil called climate change "a serious issue," saying that "action is warranted." The oil company also said it would stop funding groups that downplay the risks from global warming or lobby against measures to limit greenhouse gas emissions. While Exxon still funds 40 "skeptic groups," including the American Enterprise Institute, Cato Institute and Heritage Foundation it did cut its donations to such groups by more than 40 percent in 2006 from 2005" [210].

We need to have the individual will to overcome our fears to push for such changes. Let us hope we are getting there in the health, environmental and political sectors.

But we are able to change on at lease an individual level. And once we become aware of a problem must do so to avoid splitting. In a review of Jerome Groopman's book on how physicians think [211], editor of the *Lancet*, Richard Horton talks of the hubris of "evidence-based medicine" and the need to change [212]. Physicians can guard against these traps by heightening their sense of self-awareness and becoming conscious of their own feelings and emotions, responses, and choices.

We use heuristics when overloaded with information, when don't want to think about a problem, when stakes not important or when we have little or no information. The stakes are high for the planet we should realize that getting rid of scientism and avoiding complicity in corporate distortion and maintaining a healthy skepticism will increase credibility amongst our patients. A little thinking will actually allow us to discard a lot of irrelevant information and ultimately saves time. It will increase credibility among our patients. The same might be true for the pharmaceutical industry, for the military, for the energy sector for politicians. Looking for spin may be convincing in the short term, but in the information age of the Internet, those engaging in such behaviour have a greater risk of exposure.

CHANGE AT A SOCIETAL LEVEL

When our leaders reverse their public pronouncements as to whether Uncle Joe (Stalin), Noriega or Saddam Hussein are forces of stability, or "better than the alternative," or the "epitome of Evil" as we seek to overthrow them, populations are expected to follow these U-turns like sheep, much as we are expected to do with pharmaceutical industry failures or reversals. Now that we have seen general failures and major new threats are on the horizon,, the search for an alternative becomes more apparent.

We can even apply some of the methodologies of epidemiology and true evidence based medicine to international affairs and a preventive health based model to world affairs. Primordial Prevention in public health involves looking at root causes, the underlying disease processes, not just the proximate causes of death. In international affairs this would refer to what would normally be termed 'risk factors' for conflicts developing in the first place, addressing social causes including lack of political process, over-population, lack of education, human rights abuses, poverty and social inequalities.

Primary prevention concerns prevention in the asymptomatic phase. It would relate to preventing war or violence from breaking out when a situation of conflict already exists, or from escalating to dangerous levels. Limitation of arms, combating propaganda and diplomacy are examples of such efforts. Secondary prevention refers to the situation where war has already broken out (the disease has manifested itself) and methods to make peace are sought (peacemaking and peacekeeping). Tertiary prevention, analogous to rehabilitation in medicine and ecological restoration for environmentalists, would be post 'hot' war peace-building [213]. Using this public health model with focus on primary prevention may ultimately serve us well [214].

With non-empirical questions, an systems or ecological approach may help, recognizing feedback loops and uncertainties of risks and benefits [215]. A precautionary approach is not an unreasonable general principle[40] [216] or the Hippocratic injunction to '"First do no harm" should apply across the board to all public and private policy makers and not just to the medical profession [217, 218]. The obligation should be not on citizens and their representatives to demonstrate

---

[40]   "When an activity raises threats of harm to human health or the environment, precautionary measures should be taken even if some cause and effect relationships are not fully established scientifically. In this context the proponent of an activity, rather than the public, should bear the burden of proof. The process of applying the precautionary principle must be open, informed and democratic and must include potentially affected parties. It must also involve an examination of the full range of alternatives, including no action."

harm; rather there should be a 'Reverse Onus' [219] on those introducing new products to society to prove that the products themselves are safe, and that clean production processes are used with insignificant discharge of foreign, noxious substances. An analogous reverse onus might be appropriate for medical therapeutics and international affairs. We may allow certain latitude to deal with urgent situations, whether with using a drug with uncertain safety in a pandemic, trying to stop an imminent terrorist attack, dealing with an acute water shortage or famine or in international affairs, in the case of impending or actual genocide, but we must remain wary of those seeking to define every situation as a crisis.

The impact of a drug or therapy is especially difficult to assess more with those concerns including behavioural/social components, such as addiction, weight loss, behavioural interventions - like exercise and cognitive therapy. With these the RCT process can create a highly artificial and distorting milieu. Some have suggested that in the absence of a gold standard, we argue that a convergence of evidence from different types of studies using multiple methods of independent imperfection may provide the best bases for attributing improvements in health outcomes to interventions.[41] These may also be true for environmental or international affairs.

But even making a relatively simple decision like "Will I buy myself an ice-cream now?", all sorts of competing motivations come into play. Desire, hunger, guilt, money, obesity, fun etc. - all these thoughts jostle and compete in the mind and eventually you buy the ice-cream, or not, depending on which voices are the most persuasive at that moment in time. When the number of people involved in contributing to a decision increases, the whole process gets much more complex. Arguments get used which do not reflect the real views of the protagonist. Each voice claiming to have the public good in mind when they really are pushing their own barrow. Deconstructing/reconstructing the complex pathways leading to

---

41
   good evidence a safe and effective medicine is being appropriately prescribed; covariation between medicine use and improved health outcomes; being able to discount alternative explanations of the covariation so that medicine use is the most plausible explanation of the improved health outcomes.
   The strongest possible evidence would be provided by the coherence of the following types of evidence:
   (1) individual linked data showing that patients are prescribed the medicine, there are reasonable levels of patient compliance, and there is a relationship between medicine use and health improvements that is not explained by other factors;
   and (2) ecological evidence of improvements in these health outcomes in the population in which the medicine is used. Confidence in these inferences would be increased by: the replication of these results in comparable countries and consistent trends in population vital statistics in countries that have introduced the medicine; and epidemiological modeling indicating that changes observed in population health outcomes are plausible given the epidemiology of the condition being treated.

public interest decisions is therefore an enormously difficult task. Even powerful government committees have trouble getting to the bottom of how certain disastrous decisions got make. The PICO model of enquiry (Problem, Intervention, Comparator, Outcome) used in EBM could be employed in international affairs. I am only half-joking when I say that a Cochrane library of international or environmental interventions could truly be established [220].

Perhaps most important is a philosophical change to one of humility and - simplicity. An analysis of the increase in life expectancy over the last century in the US from 47 to 77 years shows no more than five of these years attributable to improved medical care. Much of the rest is related to public health, hygiene, education and lifestyle measures. And how much of international security vs. insecurity is really provided by national militaries?

In all fields we may have to learn to adapt and adjust to uncertainty rather than predict or control. Forest fires are often worsened by trying to eliminate smaller fires. Monoculture makes fields less sustainable and often requires more intensive care in terms of time and resources. Extremes even of hygiene, may have negative consequences such as asthma and allergies [221, 222].

In Medicine we have moved from talking about patient compliance to adherence but in terms of decision-making we have not figured out how to mesh the agenda of the patient with our science to develop a common treatment plan to which we can adhere.

A participatory, multidisciplinary approach to decision-making also can lead to more resilient decisions. Bringing all stakeholders to the table, listening to concerns and looking at joint problem solving or conflict resolution may lead to resilient decisions and a more desirable outcome, An open and transparent process establishes some level of credibility up front, though trust still needs to be earned. Such an approach might be applied to environmental and international political decision-making.

Developing a questioning attitude among the general public and advocacy through the media, to highlight these very simple errors of logic, would go a long way towards avoiding many of the past mistakes. It would not undermine the credibility of medical professionals or industry or politicians or the military but lead to joint ownership of decisions. Nothing gives more authenticity than the Truth and decision-makers from politicians to militaries to pharmaceuticals to industry can learn to be sincere.

Such efforts will lead to self-respect which occurs in traditional village inter-dependent societies.

Nobel Prize winning economist, Amartya Sen, using the criteria of number of ailments, surprisingly found that Americans self reported health was worse-much worse than Indians. Furthermore, within India it is in Kerala, the state with the highest level of life expectancy, education, empowerment of women and lowest infant mortality, where people feel the sickest, compared to the poorest state, Bihar [223].

Those in industrial societies seem to have higher rates of depression and suicide than in developing nations, which may reflect a dis-ease, a lack of empowerment or love [224]. Wealth GDP, stock indexes or oil reserves are inadequate surrogates for health and well being. The short-term drive for wealth is at the expense of the environment; the demand for oil leads to global competition and instability and may compromise health and well being.

In 2005, Australians Clive Hamilton and Richard Denniss wrote *Affluenza* asking

"if the economy has been doing so well, why are we not becoming happier?" (pvii).

"Since the early 1990s, Australia has been infected by affluenza, a growing and unhealthy preoccupation with money and material things. This illness is constantly reinforcing itself at both the individual and the social levels, constraining us to derive our identities and sense of place in the world through our consumption activity." (p178) [225]

Perhaps we could re-focus the energies of our societies on another type of prevention. Americans also spend far more on health care per person than Britons, but Britons are objectively actually healthier [226]. Our perceptions of health often bears little resemblance to the objective measures used by health officials or medical experts. Such an approach might get us to re-focus attention on real public health needs, determinants of health security well being rather than major technological glitter.[42] We could focus resources and time saved on drug

---

[42] Stephen Jay Gould from 1980 in an essay from ' The Panda's Thumb' called 'Caring Groups and Selfish genes' (p77-78):

"I think, in short, that the fascination generated by Dawkin's theory arises from some bad habits of Western scientific thought- from attitudes (pardon the jargon) that we call atomism, reductionism and determinism. The idea that the whole could be understood by decomposition into 'basic' units; that properties of microscopic units can generate and explain the behaviour of macroscopic results; that all objects and events have definitive, predictable determined causes. these ideas have been successful in our study of simple objects, made of few components, and uninfluenced by prior history.... But organisms are much more than amalgamations of genes. they have a history that matters; their parts interact in complex ways. Organisms are built by genes acting in concert, influenced by environments, translated into parts that selection sees

management towards counseling about lifestyle changes. As a society we could meet environmental and developmental challenges with resources wasted on drugs and armaments.

Cookbook medicine has little love in it. Ron McCoy, President of the Nobel Prize winning IPPNW noted,

> "A three-thousand-year tradition, which forged a bond of trust between doctor and patient, is being exchanged for a new kind of relationship. Healing is being replaced with treating; caring is being displaced by the technical management of disease; the art of listening to the patient is being supplanted by technological procedures. The human body is seen as the repository of unrelated, malfunctioning organs, often separated from the doctor's healing touch by cold, impersonal machines" [227].

Reallocating resources, time and money may allow us to put caring back into our professions and society.

---

and parts invisible to selection. Molecules that determine the properties of water are poor analogues for genes and bodies.
I may not be the master of my fate, but my intuition of wholeness probably reflects a biological truth."

CONCLUSION

Science should be seen as a tool — one of many such tools we use to make decisions.

'Scientism' is a tool of those with vested interests and undeclared biases, supported by the irrational "worship" of the trappings of science by ordinary citizens. We must be skeptical and have trained, impartial scientists with input from experts from other sectors of society and ordinary citizens to assess any information deemed "scientific." Willa Cather once said [228] *"There are only two or three human stories, and they go on repeating themselves as fiercely as if they had never happened before."* Without such input and considerations we will tragically continue to repeat mistakes in decision-making in medicine, our global environment and international affairs.

ACKNOWLEDGMENT

Thanks to Peter Mansfield, Ralph Faggotter, Joel Lexchin, Claudia Raichle, Jagjit Khosla, Anne Marie Mingiardi, John Yee, Warren Bell, David de Vidi, Jim Kutsogiannis, Jeff Nagge, Mruna Shah, Anita Greig, Gordon Guyatt, Joanna Santa Barbara, John Last, David Antebi, Sonal Singh, and for review of this paper, thoughtful comments and critical editing.

REFERENCES

[1]   Health Canada Prepulsid to be withdrawn as a result of cardiac complications May 31, 2000 http://www.hc-sc.gc.ca/ahc-asc/media/ advisories-avis/2000/2000_56_e.html

[2]   Griffin JP Prepulsid withdrawn from UK and US Markets. *Adverse Drug React Toxicol Rev.* 2000 Aug;19 (3):177.

[3]   March of Dimes Bendectin makes a Comeback http://www.marchofdimes. com/ pro fessionals/681_1820.asp

[4]   National Institutes of Health http://cerhr.niehs.nih.gov/genpub/topics/ thalidomide2-ccae.html

[5]   Rosenberg, T. "What the World Needs Now Is DDT," *New York Times Magazine* April 11, 2004

[6]   http://daphne.palomar.edu/calenvironment/ethics.htm

[7]   Holmes OW: The contagiousness of puerperal fever. N Engl Quart J Med Surg, 1842-3, 1:503-540 http://en.wikipedia.org/wiki/Oliver_Wendell_ Holmes,_Sr.

[8]   Semmelweiss IP: Die Aetiologie, der Begriff und die Prophylaxis des Kindbettfiebers. Pest, Wien und Leipzig: CA Hartleben, 1861

[9]   Lasser Karen E; Allen Paul D.; Woolhandler Steffie J.; Himmelstein David U.; Wolfe Sidney M.; Bor David H. Timing of New Black Box Warnings and Withdrawals for Prescription Medications *JAMA.* 2002;287:2215-2220. http://jama.ama-assn.org/cgi/ content/abstract/287/ 17/2215

[10]   Our Stolen Future http://www.ourstolenfuture.org/Policy/pops/2001-0522 popscon vention.htm

[11]   US Environmental Protection Agency http://www.epa.gov/international/ toxics/pop.htm

[12]   US Environmental Protection Agency Montreal Protocol on Substances that Deplete the Ozone Layer in 1987 http://www.epa.gov/ozone/title6/ phaseout /index.html

[13]   Arya N Pesticides and human health: Why Public Health officials should support a ban on non-essential residential use (Commentary) *Can. J. Public Health* March/April 2005) 89-92

[14]   Demosthenes Wisdom Quotes www.wisdomquotes.com/cat_truth.html

[15]   Arya N The end of biomilitary realism? Rethinking biomedicine and international security *Medicine Conflict and Survival* 22(3)220-229 July Sept 2006

[16]   Thomas Lewis, What Doctors Don't Know 34 (14) *New York Review of Books* September 24, 1987 http://www.nybooks.com/articles/4677

[17]   Guyatt GH. Evidence-Based Medicine[editorial]. *ACP Journal Club* 1991:A-16. (Annals of Internal Medicine; vol. 114, suppl. 2).

[18]   Dickersin Kay Straus, Sharon E Bero Lisa A Evidence based medicine: increasing, not dictating, choice *BMJ 2007;334(suppl_1):s10 (6 January)* http://www.bmj.com/cgi/content/full/334/suppl_1/s10

[19]   Sackett David L, Rosenberg William M C, Gray J A Muir, Haynes R Brian, Richardson W Scott Evidence based medicine: what it is and what it isn't It's about integrating individual clinical expertise and the best external evidence *BMJ* 1996;312:71-72 (13 January) http://www.bmj.com/ cgi/ content/full/312/7023/71

[20]   The Cochrane Collaboration www.cochrane.org

[21]   Helwig Amy, Bower Douglas, Wolff Marie, Guse Clare Residents find Clinical Practice Guidelines Valuable as Educational and Clinical Tools *Education Research and Methods* Vol 30 No 6 p 431-435

[22]   Guidelines Advisory Committee http://www.gacguidelines.ca/

[23]   Agency for Healthcare Research and Quality http://www.ahrq.gov/clinic/

[24]   National Institute for Health and Clinical Excellence http://www.nice.org. uk/

[25]   La Haute Autorité de Santé http://www.has-sante.fr

[26]   German Agency for Quality in Medicine AEZQ Leitlininien

[27]   Guidelines International http://www.g-i-n.net/

[28]   Canadian Task Force on the Periodic Health Examination: The periodic health examination. 1986 update. *Can. Med. Assoc. J.* 1986; 134: 721-729 http://www.ctfphc. org/

[29]   U.S. Preventive Services Task Force: Guide to clinical preventive services: An assessment of the effectiveness of 169 interventions. Baltimore, MD: Williams and Wilkins; 1989 http://www.ahrq.gov/clinic

[30]   Grade Working Group http://www.gradeworkinggroup.org/intro.htm

[31]   Hippocrates *On The Surgery*

[32]   Bradford Hill A "The Environment and Disease: Association or Causation?," Proceedings of the Royal Society of Medicine, 58 (1965), 295-300" http://www.edwardtufte.com/tufte/hill

[33]   Sackett David L, Rosenberg William M C, Gray J A Muir, Haynes R Brian, Richardson W Scott. Evidence based medicine: what it is and what it isn't It's about integrating individual clinical expertise and the best external evidence *BMJ* 1996;312:71-72 (13 January) http://www.bmj.com/cgi/content/full/312/7023/71

[34]   *Disease Prevention: Encyclopedia of Public Health* http://health.enotes.com/public-health-encyclopedia/disease-prevention.

[35]   Arya N Editorial Ask the Right Questions! *Ottawa Citizen* Mar. 7, 2003

[36]   Arya N. Properly Diagnose Terrorism and Work for a Just Response *Medicine and Global Survival* Feb. 2002 56-58 http://www.ippnw.org/MGS/V7N2Aftermath.pdf

[37]   Radiation Effects Research Foundation http://www.rerf.or.jp/

[38]   Sidel VW, Geiger HJ, Lown B. (1962) 'The medical consequences of thermonuclear war. II. The physician's role in the post-attack period.' *NEJM* 266:1137-45

[39]   International Physicians for the Prevention of Nuclear War www.ippnw.org

[40]   Arya N. Confronting the small arms pandemic: *Unrestricted access should be viewed as a public health disaster BMJ* 2002; 324: 990-991: (27 April) April 27, 2002 http://bmj.com/cgi/content/full/324/7344/990?eaf

[41]   Sloan J Kellermann AL et al Handgun Regulations, crime, assaults and homicide: a tale of two cities *NEJM* 1988 Nov 10:319 (19):1256-62

[42]   Kellermann, A.L., Rivara F.P.,. Rushforth N.B. "Gun ownership as a risk factor for homicide in the home", *N. Eng. J. Med.* 329, 1993: 1084-1091.

[43]   Kellermann, A.L., et al. "Suicide in the home in relation to gun ownership", *New Eng. J. Med.* 327, 1992: 467-472

[44]   Chapdelaine, A., et al. (1991) "Firearm-Related Injuries in Canada: Issues for Prevention", *CMAJ*, vol. 145, no. 10: 1217-1223.

[45]   Salvage J. (2002) 'Collateral damage: the health and environmental costs of war on Iraq.' http://www.ippnw.org/CollateralDamage.html

[46]   Arya N, Zurbrigg S. Operation Infinite Injustice: The Effect of Sanctions and Prospective War on the People of Iraq *Can J Pub Health* 94 (1) p 9-12 Jan/Feb   2003   http://www.humanities.mcmaster.ca/peace-health/Iraq comm.pdf

[47]   Iraq Body Count www.iraqbodycount.org

[48]   Roberts L Lafta R Garfield R Khudhairi J Burnham G., (2004) 'Mortality before and after the 2003 invasion of Iraq: cluster sample survey', *The Lancet*, 364 (9448), pp 1857-1864.

[49]   Burnham G, Lasta R, Doocy S, Roberts L, 2006 Mortality after the 2003 invasion of Iraq: a cross-sectional cluster sample survey *Lancet* 368:1421-28

[50]   Rossouw JE, Anderson GL, Prentice RL, LaCroix AZ, Kooperberg C, Stefanick ML, et al. Risks and benefits of estrogen plus progestin in healthy postmenopausal women: principal results from the women's health initiative randomized controlled trial. *JAMA* 2002;288: 321-33

[51]   Yang YX Lewis JD Epstein S Metz DC Long-term proton pump inhibitor therapy and risk of hip fracture. *JAMA*. 2006 Dec 27;296(24):2947-53.

[52]   Bjelakovic G, Nikolova D, Simonetti R Mortality in Randomized Trials of Antioxidant Supplements for Primary and Secondary Prevention: Systematic Review and Metaanalysis. *JAMA*. 2007; 297: 842-857 http://jama.ama-assn.org/cgi/content/full/297/ 8/842

[53]   Hirvonen Tero,; Virtamo Jarmo, ; Korhonen Pasi, ; Albanes Demetrius,; Pietinen Pirjo, Alpha-Tocopherol, Beta Carotene Cancer Prevention Study Group. The effect of vitamin E and beta carotene on the incidence of lung cancer and other cancers in male smokers. *New England Journal of Medicine* 1994 Apr 14;330(15):1029-1035

[54]   Yusuf S, Dagenais G, Pogue J, Bosch J, Sleight P. Vitamin E supplementation and cardiovascular events in high-risk patients. The Heart Outcomes Prevention Evaluation Study Investigators. *N. Engl. J. Med.* 2000;342(3):154-160

[55]   Omenn GS, Goodman GE, Thornquist MD, Balmes J, Cullen MR, Glass A, Keogh JP,Meyskens FL, Valanis B, Williams JH, Barnhart S, Hammar S. Effects of a combination of beta carotene and vitamin A on lung cancer and cardiovascular disease.*N. Engl. J. Med..* 1996 May 2;334(18):1150-5.

[56]   Beta Carotene Cancer Prevention Study Group. *N Engl J Med* 1994;330(15) 1029-1035.

[57]   Fleming, Thomas R and Demets David L. Surrogate End Points in Clinical Trials: Are We Being Misled? *Annals* 125- (7) 605-613 1 October 1996 http://www.annals.org/cgi/content/full/125/7/605

[58]   Echt DS, Liebson PR, Mitchell LB, Peters RW, Obias-Manno D, Barker AH, et al. Mortality and morbidity in patients receiving encainide, flecainide, or placebo. The cardiac arrhythmia suppression trial. *N. Engl. J. Med.* 1991;324: 781-8

[59]   CAST Investigators. Preliminary report: effect of encainide and flecainide on mortality in a randomized trial of arrhythmia suppression after myocardial infarction. *N. Engl. J. Med.* 1989, 321: 406-412.

[60]   The Cardiac Arrhythmia Suppression Trial II Investigators. Effect of the antiarrhythmic agent moricizine on survival after myocardial infarction. *N. Engl. J. Med.* 1992; 327:227-33.

[61]   Nissen SE and Wolski K. Effect of rosiglitazone on the risk of myocardial infarction and death from Cardiovascular Causes. *N. Engl. J. Med.* 2007 Jun 14;[e-pub ahead of print]. (http://content.nejm.org/cgi/content/full/NEJM oa072761)

[62]   Singh Sonal Loke Yoon K Furberg Curt D Emerging safety concerns with the – time for urgent regulatory action *Lancet*

[63]   Gerstein HC, Yusuf S, Bosch J, Pogue J, Sheridan P, et al. Effect of rosiglitazone on the frequency of diabetes in patients with impaired glucose tolerance or impaired fasting glucose: A randomised controlled trial. *Lancet* /2006; 368:1096-1105.

[64]   Nissen SE. The DREAM trial. Diabetes Reduction Assessment with ramipril and rosiglitazone Medication, *Lancet*/ 2006; 368:2049

[65]   Committee of Principal Investigators W.H.O. cooperative trial on primary prevention of ischaemic heart disease using clofibrate to lower serum cholesterol: mortality follow-up. *Lancet.* 1980 Aug 23; 2(8191):379-85.

[66]   Coronary Drug Project Research Group. Clofibrate and niacin in coronary heart disease. *JAMA.* 1975; 231:360-81

[67]   Scandinavian Simvastatin Survival Study (4S). Group.Randomised trial of cholesterol lowering in 4444 patients with coronary heart disease: *Lancet.* 1994; 344:1383-9.

[68]   Hayward Rodney A Hofer Timothy P Vijan Sandeep Narrative Review: Lack of Evidence for Recommended Low-Density Lipoprotein Treatment Targets: A Solvable Problem *Annals of Internal Medicine* 3 October 2006 Volume 145 Issue 7 | Pages 520-530 http://www.annals.org/cgi/content/abstract/145/7/520

[69]   Huang X, Chen H, Miller WC, Mailman RB, Woodard JL, Chen PC, Xiang D, Murrow RW, Wang YZ, Poole C. Lower low-density lipoprotein cholesterol levels are associated with Parkinson's disease. *Movement Disorders* 2007 Feb 15;22(3):377-81.

[70]   "Bayer Voluntarily Withdraws Baycol," U.S. Food and Drug Administration Talk Paper: www.fda.gov/bbs/topics/ANSWERS/2001/ANS01095.html JP Griffin The withdrawal of Baycol (cerivastatin). *Adverse Drug React Toxicol Rev.* 2001 Dec;20(4):177-80.

[71]   Collins R, Peto R, MacMahon S, Hebert P, Fiebach NH, Eberlein KA, et al. Blood pressure, stroke, and coronary heart disease. Part 2, Short-term reductions in blood pressure: overview of randomized drug trials in their epidemiological context. *Lancet.* 1990; 335:827-38.

[72]   Hypertension Detection and Follow-up Program Cooperative Group. Five-year findings of the hypertension detection and follow-up program. I. Reduction in mortality of persons with high blood pressure, including mild hypertension. *JAMA.* 1979; 242:2562-71.

[73]   ALLHAT Collaborative Research Group. Major cardiovascular events in hypertensive patients randomized to doxazosin vs chlorthalidone:the antihypertensive and lipid lowering treatment to prevent heart attack trial (ALLHAT). *JAMA* 2000 April 19; 283:15: 1967-1975.http://www.nhlbi.nih.gov/health/allhat/qckref.htm

[74]   Psaty BM, Heckbert SR, Koepsell TD, Siscovick DS, et al. The risk of myocardial infarction associated with antihypertensive drug therapies. *JAMA* 1995;274:620-5.

[75]   Held PH, Yusuf S, Furberg CD. Calcium channel blockers in acute myocardial infarction and unstable angina: an overview. *BMJ* 1989; 299: 1187-9

[76]   Yusuf S, Held PH, Furberg CD. Update of effects of calcium antagonists in myocardial infarction or angina in light of the Second Danish Verapamil Infarction Trial (DAVIT-II) and other recent studies. *Am. J. Cardiol.* 1991; 67: 1295-7.

[77]   Wald NJ Law MR A strategy to reduce cardiovascular disease by more than 80% *BMJ* 2003;326:1419 (28 June) http://bmj.bmjjournals.com/cgi/content/full/326/7404/1419

[78]   *Reddy K. Srinath* The Preventive Polypill — Much Promise, Insufficient Evidence *NEJM* 356 (3) :212 Jan 18, 2007 http://content.nejm.org/cgi/content/full/356/3/212

[79]   Faggotter Ralph Feb 7, 2006 Personal Correspondence.

[80]   Taylor Rosie and Giles Jim Cash interests taint drug advice *Nature* Vol 437|20 October 2005, page 1070 http://www.nature.com/nature/journal/v437/n7062/index.html doi: 10.1038/4371070a

[81]   Zappa Frank, Album: Joe's Garage, Track: Packard Goose

[82]   Hampton JR. Evidence-based medicine, opinion-based medicine, and real-world medicine. *Perspect Biol. Med.* 2002 Fall;45(4):549-68.

[83]   Holmes D,1 Murray SJ, Perron A, Rail G. Deconstructing the evidence-based discourse in health sciences: truth, power and fascism. *Int. J. Evid. Based Healthcare*2006; 4: 180–186

[84]   Mansfield P. Industry-Sponsored Research: A More Comprehensive Alternative. *PLoS Med.* 2006;3(10): e463 http://medicine.plosjournals.org/perlserv/?request=get-ocumentanddoi=10.1371/journal.pmed.0030463

[85]   Genuis Stephen J. The Proliferation of Clinical Practice Guidelines: Professional Development or Medicine-by-Numbers? *The Journal of the American Board of Family Practice* 18:419-425 (2005) http://www.jabfm. org/cgi/ content/full/18/5/419

[86]   Sackett David L, Rosenberg William M C, Gray J A Muir, Haynes R Brian, Richardson W Scott Evidence based medicine: what it is and what it isn't It's about integrating individual clinical expertise and the best external evidence *BMJ* 1996;312:71-72 (13 January) http://www.bmj.com/cgi/ content/full/312/7023/71

[87]   Faggotter Ralph MD personal correspondence Biojest Nov 11, 2006

[88]   Lexchin J et al. Pharmaceutical industry sponsorship and research outcome and quality: Systematic review. *BMJ* 2003 May 31; 326:1167-70. http://www.bmj.com/cgi/reprint/326/7400/1167.pdf

[89]   Hughes Michael D Williams Paige L Challenges in Using Observational Studies to Evaluate Adverse Effects of Treatment *NEJM* 356(17) 1705-1707 April 26,2007

[90]   Ware James H The Limitations of Statistical Methods as Prognostic Tools *NEJM* 355:25 2015-2017 Dec 21, 2006

[91]   Rothwell PM. External validity of randomised controlled trials: "to whom do the results of this trial apply?". *Lancet.* 2005 Jan 1;365(9453):82-93.

[92]   Hall Wayne D Lauke Jayne Assessing the impact of prescribed medicines on health outcomes *Australia and New Zealand Health Policy* 2007, 4:1 http://www.anzhealthpolicy.com/content/pdf/1743-8462-4-1.pdf

[93]   Groll, D.L. and Thomson, D.J. (2006) Incidence of influenza in Ontario following the Universal Influenza Immunization Campaign. *Vaccine*, 24(24), 5245-5250

[94]   Haynes RB, Sackett DL. Taylor DW Gibson ES Johnson AL. lncreased absenteeism from work after detection and labelling of hypertensive patients. *N. Engl. J. Med.* 1978;299:741-4.

[95]   Prentice and Lind, "Fetal heart rate monitoring during labor-- too frequent intervention, too little benefit"[1987:2:1375-1377]

[96]   Baxter, Nancy, with the Canadian Task Force on Preventive Health Care, "Preventive Health Care, 2001 Update: Should Women Be Routinely Taught Breast Self-Examination to Screen for Breast Cancer?" *Can. Med. Assoc. Jrnl.* 2001;164(13):1837-1846. June 26, 2001. http://www.cmaj.ca/cgi/reprint/164/13/1837

[97]   Canadian Task Force on the Periodic Health Examination, the CTFPHC http://www.ctfphc.org

[98]   Miller AB, To T, Baines CJ, et al. Canadian National Breast Screening Study-2: 13-year results of a randomized trial in women aged 50-59 years. *J. Natl. Cancer Inst.* 2000;92(18):1490-1499

[99]   Miller AB, Baines CJ, To T, Wall C. Canadian National Breast Screening Study: 1. Breast cancer detection and death rates among women aged 40 to 49 years. *CMAJ.* 1992;147(10):1459-1476.

[100] International Health News http://vvv.com/healthnews/mammography.html

[101] Canadian Women's Health Network http://www.cwhn.ca/resources/afi/mammograms. html

[102] Olsen O, Gøtzsche PC. Systematic review of screening for breast cancer with mammography (Gøtzsche PC. Screening for breast cancer with mammography. *Lancet* 2001; 358: 2167-2168

[103] Horton R. Screening mammography—setting the record straight. *Lancet* 2002; 359: 441-442

[104] Ibid. from Jorgensen, KJ and Gotzsche, PC. Presentation on websites of possible benefits and harms from screening for breast cancer: cross sectional study. *British Medical Journal*, Vol. 328, January 17, 2004, pp. 148-53

[105] Wolf AM, Nasser JF, Wolf AM, Schorling JB. The impact of informed consent on patient interest in prostate-specific antigen screening. *Arch Intern. Med.* 1996; 156: 1333-1336 http://bmj.bmjjournals.com/cgi/content/full/325/7357/216

[106] Feightner John W. Canadian Task Force on Preventive Health Care http://www.ctfphc.org/Full_Text/Ch67full.htm.

[107] Stanford JL, Feng Z, Hamilton AS, Gilliland FD, Stephenson RA, Eley JW, et al. Urinary and sexual function after radical prostatectomy for clinically localized prostate cancer: the Prostate Cancer Outcomes Study. *JAMA* 2000; 283: 354-360

[108] Del Mar Chris Asymptomatic haematuria ...in the doctor, *BMJ* 2000; 320: 165-166 (15 January)

[109] US National Cancer Institute http://www.cancer.gov/clinicaltrials/results/mayo-lung-project0800

[110] Marcus, P.M., Bergstralh, E.J., Fagerstrom, R.M., Williams, D.E., Fontana, R., Taylor, W.F., Prorok, P.C. (2000, August 16). Lung cancer mortality in the Mayo Lung Project: Impact of extended follow-up. *Journal of the National Cancer Institute, 92*(16), 1308-1316. Aug 16, 2000

[111] Henschke Claudia I. Yankelevitz David F. Libby Daniel M.,Pasmantier Mark W., and Smith James P., Miettinen Olli S. Survival of Patients with Stage I Lung Cancer Detected on CT Screening *NEJM* http://content.nejm. org/cgi/content/abstract/355/17/1763

[112] Kolata Gina Researchers Dispute Benefits of CT Scans for Lung Cancer *New York Times* March 7, 2007 http://www.nytimes.com/2007/03/07/health/07lung.html

[113] Bach Peter B Jett James R Pastorino Ugo Tockman Melvyn S Swensen Stephen J Begg Colin B Computed Tomography Screening and Lung Cancer Outcomes *Journal of the American Association JAMA* 2007; 297: 953-961. http://jama.ama-assn.org/cgi/content/abstract/297/9/953

[114] Miser William F. To Treat or Not to Treat Otitis Media - That's Just One of the Questions *Journal of the American Board of Family Practic*

[115] Rosenfeld RM, Vertrees JE, Carr J, Cipolle RJ, Uden DL, Giebink GS, et al. Clinical efficacy of antimicrobial drugs for acute otitis media: meta-analysis of 5400 children from thirty-three randomized trials. *J. Pediatr.* 1994; 124: 355-

[116] Van Buchem FL, Dunk JHM, van't Hof MA. Appelman CLM, Claessen JQPJ, Touw-Otten FWMM, Hordijk GJ, de Melker RA. Co-amoxiclav in recurrent acute otitis media: placebo controlled study. *BMJ* 1991; 303: 1450-

[117] Burke P, Bain J, Robinson D, Dunleavy J. Acute red ear in children: controlled trial of non-antibiotic treatment in general practice. *BMJ* 1991; 303: 558-562

[118] Boden W. E., O'Rourke R. A., Teo K. K., Hartigan P. M., Maron D. J., Kostuk W. J., Knudtson M., Dada M., Casperson P., Harris C. L., Chaitman B. R., Shaw L., Gosselin G., Nawaz S., Title L. M., Gau G., Blaustein A. S., Booth D. C., Bates E. R., Spertus J. A., Berman D. S., Mancini G.B. J., Weintraub W. S., the COURAGE Trial Research Group Optimal Medical Therapy with or without PCI for Stable Coronary Disease *N. Engl. J. Med.* 2007; www.nejm.org on Mar 26, 2007 (10.1056/NEJMoa070829 April 12, 2007 print

[119] Satel Sally and Hoff Sommers Christina The Mental Health Crisis That Wasn't: How the trauma industry exploited 9/11 *Reason* On-line August/September 2005 http://www.reason.com/0508/fe.ss.the.shtml

[120] Hobbs M, Mayou R, Harrison B, Worlock P. A randomised controlled trial of psychological debriefing for victims of road traffic accidents. *BMJ* 1996;313: 1438-9

[121] Enkin Murray Keirse Marc JNC Neilson James Crowther Caroline Duley Lelia,, Hodnett Ellen, Hofmneyr G. Justus Effective Care In Pregnancy and Childbirth: A Synopsis Chapter 50 in *A Guide to Effective Care in Pregnancy and Childbirth* 2000 Oxford University Press 2000 http://www. collegeofmidwives.org/prof_articles01/

[122] Andrew MH, Roty AR Jr. Incidental appendectomy with cholecystectomy: is the increased risk justified. *Am Surg* 1987 Oct;53(10):553-7 found at http://www.qualitymeasures.ahrq.gov/summary /summary.aspx?ss=2anddoc_id=6661

[123] Lambert M.L.Cholecystectomy and appendectomy utilisation rates in Belgium: trends 1986-1996 and impact of laparoscopic surgery. Cholecystectomy rates increased by 64% over 7 years (1989 1996) following the introduction of laparoscopic surgery. Appendectomy rates per 100.000 showed a remarkably steady decrease from 282,3 in 1986 to 166,4 in 1996 Belgian trends parallel those observed elsewhere. http://www.iph.fgov.be/aph/abstr200058233240.htm

[124] Jentleson, Bruce. 2000. American Foreign Policy: The Dynamics of Choice in the 21st Century. New York : W.W. Norton and Co.

[125] Mead Walter Russell, "The Case Against Europe The very things that Europeans think make their political judgment better than Americans' actually make it worse", The Atlantic Monthly, 289(4), 2002, p. 26, available at http://globetrotter.berkeley.edu/people3/Mead/meadcon3.html

[126] Kagan Robert *Of Paradise and Power, America and Europe in the New World Order* Alfred A Knopf, New York, 2003

[127] Gray, John Men Are from Mars, Women Are from Venus: A Practical Guide for Improving Communication and Getting What You Want in Your Relationships Harper Collins 1992

[128] Bergen Peter Cruickshank Paul Iraq 101: The Iraq Effect - War has increased Terrorism Seven-fold Worldwide http://www.motherjones. com/news/featurex/2007/03/iraq_effect_1.html Sengupta Kim Cockburn Patrick The War on Terror Is the Leading Cause of Terrorism *The Independent* UK. March 1, 2007. http://www.alternet.org/waroniraq/ 48620/

[129] Arya N Is military action ever justified? : A Physician Defends the Responsibility to Protect *Medicine Conflict and Survival* 23 (3)

[130] US National Weather Service http://www.lightningsafety.noaa.gov/medical.htm

[131] US National Safety Council http://www.nsc.org/lrs/statinfo/odds.htm

[132] Kahneman Daniel, Renshon Jonathan Why Hawks Win January/February 2007 January 15, 2007 http://www.foreignpolicy.com/story/cms.php?story_id=3660

[133] Holt Jim The Human Factor *New York Times* March 28, 2004 http://www.nytimes.com/2004/03/28/magazine/28WWLN.html

[134] Greenhalgh Trisha, Kostopoulou Olga, Harries Clare *BMJ* 2004;329:47-50(3 July), Making decisions about benefits and harms of medicines http://bmj.bmjjournals.com/cgi/content/full/329/7456/47

[135] Engelhardt Tom 9/11 Life Worth $1.8 million; Iraqi Life, $2,000. What Does It Mean? *Alternet* May 15, 2007 http://www.alternet.org/story/51886/

[136] Herxheimer A (2005) Communicating with Patients about Harms and Risks. *PLoS Med.* 2(2): e42 February 22, 2005 http://medicine.plosjournals.org/perlserv/?request=get-documentanddoi=10.1371/journal.pmed.0020042

[137] McNeil BJ Pauker SG Sox HC Jr. Tversky A On the elicitation of preferences for alternative therapies. *NEJM* 1982 May 27;306 (21):1259-62

[138] Gladwell Malcolm Blink: The Power of Thinking Without Thinking Brown Little 2005

[139] Vioxx Recalled Sept 30, 2005 http://www.adrugrecall.com/ US Food and Drug Administration http://www.fda.gov/cder/drug/infopage/vioxx/vioxxQA.htm

[140] US Food and Drug Administration http://www.fda.gov/medwatch/SAFETY/2005/safety05.htm#Bextra

[141] Borger Julian Wake-up call *The Guardian* Friday September 6, 2002 http://www.guardian.co.uk/g2/story/0,3604,786992,00.html

[142] Groopman Jerome *How Doctors Think* Houghton Mifflin

[143] Dyer Owen Breast CA: who should be scanned? New MRI and mammography guidelines send mixed messages *National Review of Medicine* 4(8) April 30, 2007 http://www.nationalreviewofmedicine.com/issue/2007/04_30/4_patients_practice_8.html

[144]   Doust Jenny, Del Mar Chris Why do doctors use treatments that do not
        work? *BMJ* 2004;328:474-475 (28 February), http://bmj.bmjjournals.com/
        cgi/content/full/328/74 38/474

[145]   Kahneman Daniel, Renshon Jonathan Why Hawks Win *Foreign Policy*
        January/February 2007 January 15, 2007 http://www.foreignpolicy.com/
        story/cms.php? story_id=3660

[146]   Simon, Herbert A. 1997. Models of Bounded Rationality. Volume 3.
        Empirically Grounded Economic Reason. Cambridge, Massachusetts: The
        MIT Press quoted in Odell John S. Bounded rationality and the World
        Political Economy: The Nature of Decision Making Chapter 11 in
        Governing the World's Money, ed. David M. Andrews, C. Randall
        Henning, and Louis W. Pauly (Cornell University Press, 2002 http://www-
        rcf.usc.edu/~odell/text%20092101%20web.doc

[147]   Barber Benjamin R Jihad vs McWorld *The Atlantic Monthly* March 1992
        http://www.theatlantic.com/doc/199203/barber

[148]   Scott Tim Stanford Neil Thompson David R, Images of health Killing me
        softly: myth in pharmaceutical advertising *BMJ* 2004;329:1484-1487 (18
        December),   doi:10.1136/bmj.329.7480.1484   http://www.bmj.com/cgi/
        content/ full/329/7480/1484

[149]   Quoted in PR Watch http://www.prwatch.org/prwissues/2003Q1/monger.
        html

[150]   Payer L. Disease-mongers: How doctors, drug companies and insurers are
        making you feel sick. New York: John Wiley, and Sons 1992.

[151]   Malleson Andrew Whiplash and Other Useful Illnesses McGill-Queen's
        University Press (April, 2002) reviewed Brian Grottkau, M.D.New
        England   Journal   of   Medicine,   April   3,   2003
        http://content.nejm.org/cgi/content/full/ 348/14/1413

[152]   Diseasemongering *PLOS* April 2006 http://collections.plos.org/
        diseasemongering-2006.php

[153]   Moynihan R, Heath I, Henry D. Selling sickness: the pharmaceutical
        industry and disease mongering. *BMJ* 2002; 324: 886-891

[154]   Cassels Alan Moynihan Ray Pharmaceuticals for healthy people US:
        selling   to   the   worried   well   *Le   Monde   Diplomatique*
        http://mondediplo.com/ 2006/05/16bigpharma May 2006 adapted from
        their book *'Selling Sickness. How Drug Companies Are Turning Us All
        into Patients' (Allen and Unwin, 2005)*

[155]   Moynihan R. The making of a disease: female sexual dysfunction *BMJ*
        2003;326:45-47(4January)
        http://bmj.bmjjournals.com/cgi/content/full/326/ 7379/45

[156] Tiefer Leonore Female Sexual Dysfunction: A Case Study of Disease Mongering and Activist Resistance *PLOS Medicine* www[losmedicine.org April 2006 3 (4) e 178-182

[157] Kolata Gina If You've Got a Pulse, You're Sick *New York Times* May 21, 2006 http://www.nytimes.com/2006/05/21/weekinreview/21kolata.html

[158] Michaels, David Living in a Chemical World: Framing the Future in Light of the Past Volume 1076 published September 2006 *Ann. N.Y. Acad. Sci.* 1076: 149–162 (2006). doi: 10.1196/annals.1371.058 http://www.annalsnyas.org/cgi/content/abstract/1076/1/149

[159] Michaels, David, *DOUBT Is Their Product Scientific American*, Jun2005, Vol. 292, Issue 6

[160] Doll R, Hill AB: Smoking and carcinoma of the lung; preliminary report. *Br. Med. J*, 1950, 2:739-748;

[161] Doll R, Hill AB. The mortality of doctors in relation to their smoking habits. *Br. Med. J.* 1954;228:1451-5. Reproduced in: BMJ 2004;328:1529-3

[162] International Journal of Occupational and Environmental Health http://www.ijoeh.com/ SPECIAL ISSUE Volume II, Number 4 October - December 2005 Feature: Corporate Corruption of Science

[163] Gustave Gilbert "Nürnberger Tagebuch." Nuremberg Diary 18 April 1946 http://www.snopes.com/quotes/goering.htm

[164] Center for Media and Democracy Submitted by Diane Farsetta on Fri, 05/11/2007 http://www.prwatch.org/node/6034

[165] *The European Journal of the History of Economic Thought*, Routledge Volume 8, Issue 1 March 2001, pages 105 - 117

[166] DoD News Briefing - Secretary Rumsfeld and Gen. Pace http://www.dod.gov/transcripts/2001/t12212001_t1221sd.html

[167] Needless Surgery *Consumer Reports on Health* (March 1998) http://www.quackwatch.org/04ConsumerEducation/crhsurgery.html

[168] Bekelman Justin E., Yan Li AB Gross Cary P.Scope and Impact of Financial Conflicts of Interest in Biomedical Research A Systematic Review *JAMA* 2003;289:454-465. Jan 22

[169] Kei Koizumi Chapter 6 RandD in the FY 2005 Department of Defense Budget American Association for the Advancement of Science REPORT XXIX RESEARCH AND DEVELOPMENT FY 2005 (2004) http://www.aaas.org/spp/rd/05pch6.htm

[170] SIPRI *Stockholm International Peace Research Institute* Yearbook 2005 http://yearbook2005.sipri.org/highl/highlights

[171]   Hartung William *World Policy Institute* ARMS TRADE RESOURCE
        CENTER REPORTS - Peddling Arms, Peddling Influence: Exposing the
        Arms Export Lobby October 1996 World Policy http://www.worldpolicy.
        org/projects/arms/reports/papi2rep. html

[172]   Oil Company Spent Nearly $16 Million to Fund Skeptic Groups, Create
        Confusion ExxonMobil Report Jan 3, 2007 Smoke, Mirrors and Hot Air:
        How ExxonMobil Uses Big Tobacco's Tactics to "Manufacture
        Uncertainty" on Climate Change

[173]   JunkScience.com

[174]   Brandt Allan"The Cigarette Century http://www.cigarettecentury.com/
        index.html

[175]   *AlterNet, April 16, 2007* http://www.alternet.org/mediaculture/50359/

[176]   Beder Sharon Gosden WPP: World Propaganda Power PR Watch 8(2)
        2001 Richard http://www.prwatch.org/prwissues/2001Q2/wpp.html

[177]   Corporate Watch July 2002 http://www.corporatewatch.org.uk/?lid=395

[178]   Cox Teri R Forging Alliances *Pharmaceutical Executive* Magazine,
        September 1, 2002. http://www.pharmexec.com/pharmexec/article/article
        Detail.jsp?id=29974

[179]   Burton Bob Rowell Andy Quoted in From Patient Activism to Astroturf
        Marketing *PR Watch* 4(1) 1997 http://www.prwatch.org/prwissues/
        2003Q1/astroturf.html Quoted in Burton Bob Rowell Andy Disease
        Mongering PR Watch 10(1) 2003 http://www.prwatch.org/prwissues/
        2003Q1/monger.html

[180]   Mammography information questioned http://vvv.com/healthnews/
        mammography.html

[181]   Moynihan et al. Op cit.

[182]   Source Watch http://www.sourcewatch.org/index.php?title=Front_groups

[183]   Fialka John Another Filthy Front Group *Wall Street Journal* April 27,
        2007 http://online.wsj.com/article/SB117763193289184191.html

[184]   International Atomic Energy Agency http://www.iaea.org/About/statute
        _text.html

[185]   Goldenberg Suzanne Bush administration accused of doctoring scientists'
        reports on climate change *The Guardian* Wednesday January 31, 2007
        http://www.guardian.co.uk/usa/story/0,,2002484,00.html

[186]   Rumsfeld Donald http://sadlyno.com/archives/000497.html

[187]   Rosenstock IM 1974 http://www.comminit.com/changetheories/ctheories/
        changetheories-31.html

[188]   Bandura, A. (1977). *Social Learning Theory*. New York: General
        Learning Press.

[189] Last JM: The Future of Public Health. *Japanese Journal of Public Health*, 1991, 38:10:58-93

[190] Rumsfeld Donald Department of Defense news briefing Feb. 12, 2002, http://www.brainyquote.com/quotes/quotes/d/donaldrums148142.html

[191] Angell Marcia The Truth About the Drug Companies *New York Review of Books* http://www.nybooks.com/articles/17244

[192] 29 September 2006 http://open.imshealth.com/

[193] Angell M. The pharmaceutical industry: to whom is it accountable? *New Engl. J. Med.* 342: 1902-4. http://content.nejm.org/cgi/content/full/342/25/1902

[194] Arya N Letter Reasons to be Fearful *Time* September 23, 2002 http://www.time.com/time/magazine/article/0,9171,1003298-4,00.html http://www.time.com/time/magazine/ article/0,9171,1101020923-351218-2,00.html

[195] Rumsfeld Donald Press conference at NATO headquarters, Brussels, Belgium, June 6, 2002," US Department of Defense The Acronym Institute. transcript. www.acronym.org.uk/docs/0206/doc04.htm

[196] Avalon Project Yale University http://www.yale.edu/lawweb/avalon/presiden/speeches/eisenhower001.htm

[197] Bacevich Andrew J. The New American Militarism: How Americans Are Seduced By War Oxford University Press, 2005 http://www.thirdworldtraveler.com/American_Empire/Wilsonians_TNAM.html

[198] Anonymous friend Personal correspondence May 15, 2007

[199] Gladwell Malcolm The Tipping Point: How Little Things Can Make a Big Difference Little Brown 2000

[200] Prochasta James O Norcross John C and Diclemente Carlo C Changing for Good: The Revolutionary Program That Explains the Six Stages of Change and Teaches You How to Free Yourself from Bad Habits

[201] Beck, Aaron T., "Cognitive Models of Depression," in *Journal of Cognitive Psychotherapy,* Vol. 1, No. 1, 1987, pp. 5-37.

[202] *New York Times, May 8, 2007* http://www.nytimes.com/2007/05/08/world/asia/09 afghancnd.html

[203] Haditha Investigations Suggest Military Cover-Up *New York Times, May 6, 2007* http://www.nytimes.com/2007/05/06/world/middleeast/06haditha.htm

[204] http://www.prwatch.org/prissues/1997Q1/risky.html

[205] Rosenblum Jonathan Tracking the Front Group "Boomerang," posted Wed, 03/14/2007 http://www.prwatch.org/node/5847

[206]   Stauber John and Rampton Sheldon *Toxic Sludge is Good for You* (Common Courage Press, 1995),

[207]   Pfau Michael, Haigh Michel, Sims Jeanetta and Wrigley Shelley "The Influence of Corporate Front-Group Stealth Campaigns *Communications Research* February 2007

[208]   http://www.nrc.gov/reading-rm/basic-ref/glossary/risk-based-decisionmaking.html

[209]   Risky Business: The World According to Hill and Knowlton *PR Watch* 4(1) 1997

[210]   Reuters, May 18, 2007 http://www.reuters.com/article/environmentNews/idUSN18439 60820070518

[211]   Groopman Jerome *How Doctors Think* Houghton Mifflin

[212]   Horton Richard What's Wrong with Doctors *New York Review of Books* 54(9)· May 31, 2007 http://www.nybooks.com/articles/20214

[213]   Yusuf S, Anand S, MacQueen G. (1998) 'Can medicine prevent war?' *BMJ*; 317: 1669-70. Dec Website. Online. Available: http://bmj.com/cgi/content/ full/317/7174/1669.

[214]   Arya N. Do no harm: towards a Hippocratic standard for international civilization for 'The end of Westphalia? Re-envisioning sovereignty' for United Nations. Presentation for University Nations University/ Griffith University Key Centre for Governance April 8-10, 2005 at Canberra Australian National University

[215]   Arya N Howard J et al Time for an ecosystem approach to public health? Lessons from two infectious disease outbreaks in Canada *Global Public Health* July 2007

[216]   Science and Environmental Health Network - Wingspread Statement on the Precautionary Principle, Jan. 1998. http://www.sehn.org/precaution.html

[217]   Arya Neil Do No Harm: Towards a Hippocratic Standard for International Civilization in Re-envisioning Sovereignty Ramesh Thakur and Charles Sampford ed 2007

[218]   Arya N. Healing our Planet: Physicians and Global Security *Croatian Medical Journal CMJ* 44 (2) 139-147 March April 2003 http://www.cmj.hr/index.php?D=/44/2/139

[219]   Die Off http://dieoff.org/page31.htm Interpreting the Principle

[220]   Faggotter Ralph Personal Correspondence May 9. 2007

[221]   Sherriff, A Golding J and The Alspac Study Team Hygiene levels in a contemporary population cohort are associated with wheezing and atopic eczema in preschool infants *Archives of Disease in Childhood* 2002;87:26-29 http://adc.bmj.com/cgi/content/ abstract/87/1/26

[222]   von Mutius Erika The Increase in Asthma Can Be Ascribed to Cleanliness *Am. J. Respir. Crit. Care Med.*, Volume 164, Number 7, October 2001, 1106-1107 http://ajrccm.atsjournals.org/cgi/content/full/164/7/1106

[223]   Sen Amartya Health: perception versus observation *BMJ* 2002;324:860-861 (13 April) http://bmj.bmjjournals.com/cgi/content/full/324/7342/860

[224]   The WHO World Mental Health Survey Consortium Prevalence, Severity, and Unmet Need for Treatment of Mental Disorders in the World Health Organization World Mental Health Surveys, *Journal of the American Medical Association* 291 (21) 2 June 2004 http://jama.ama-assn.org/cgi/content/full/291/21/2581

[225]   'Affluenza' . see-http://en.wikipedia.org/wiki/Affluenza

[226]   Marmot Michael Oldfield Zoe Smith James P Disease and Disadvantage in the United States and England James Banks *JAMA* 2006:295 2037-2045

[227]   McCoy Ronald S. Restoring the Soul of Medicine Oration given at the annual general meeting of the Malaysian Medical Association on 13 June 2002

[228]   Cather Willa Carl in '*Oh Pioneers*' Houghton Mifflin 1913.

INDEX

C

Q

R

S

Y

Z